Rise Up Shine On

By
Leann Rhodes

Rise Up Shine On
Copyright © 2016 by Leann Rhodes

Author's Note:

This story is based on Leann's recollections of the moments in her life that molded her into the woman she is today. Leann found the light inside of herself even when darkness often surrounded her.
Leann chose to embrace love instead of fear.

It should be noted that names and places have been changed throughout this book in order to protect the privacy of those involved. This story is too important to stay in the shadows; it's time to share the lessons with others.

As you read Leann's story, reflect on your own inner light so that you can shine brightly for all to see.

Dedication

This book is dedicated to Madison.

I want you to grow up to be a strong, independent woman.

I want you to always treat others the way you want to be treated.

Shoot for every dream you have.

Always let your inner light shine throughout your whole life and, most importantly, never forget: you are loved!

-Preface-

The wooden steps creaked beneath her as she shifted her small frame. She could feel the ridges of the planks through her thin summer clothes as she leaned forward to hug her legs. Her gaunt frame folded onto itself as she curled forward into a ball. There, she sat alone in the dark.

There was nowhere to look; the basement was one, giant concrete room. No lights, no windows. She had already been down there for hours, waiting for the call from her father that would mean her release.

Suddenly the routine noises from the family upstairs quieted as a heavy door slammed closed. In that same moment, she turned hopefully to the door at the top of the stairs. The door that blocked her from daylight, from other humans, and from freedom was still solidly closed. It firmly stood over her, blocking out almost all light and connection.

Except for one small line of yellow. There was complete darkness except for the slight gap between the bottom of the door and the kitchen tile. In that space, some late-morning sunshine reflected off the ceramic floor, and announced itself confidently even though it was such a narrow space. That light was so warm and gentle that she decided to unfold herself. And then, for several minutes, she actually considered moving out of the darkness.

She finally allowed herself to stretch and turn towards the light that was offered at the top of the unfinished stairs.

And then it happened: she decided to risk leaving her assigned place to get closer to the light, to allow it to soothe her. She turned her back to the darkness and focused on what lay ahead.

Slowly she put one hand, then another, on the steps in front of her. One step at a time, she crawled upwards. She knew which wooden planks creaked, and avoided them carefully so she wouldn't make a sound.

A smile started to form on her face as she realized the light above had warmth as well. It beckoned her as she got closer and closer still. The light cheered her on lovingly until she finally rested her chin on the top step.

It was the most comfort she had felt in hours. The slice of light offered itself without rules, threats, or consequence. She felt at peace, knowing that she could still find unconditional goodness, even as lonely darkness surrounded her.

It has to get better, she thought to herself.

"Just wait," a voice whispered in her mind.

Leann smiled slightly.

She could wait.

Chapter 1

"Love the addict;
hate the addiction."

The memories of one's early years are always snapshots; quick glimpses of specific moments that have no backstory or follow-up to provide a complete picture. They pop up unexpectedly and hurl you back in time without apology or explanation. Eventually you can patch together a mental collage of your childhood and see the pivotal moments shining brightly. They aren't always sweet cuddly memories; instead, they're often the experiences that introduced our strongest emotions. Sometimes love, but often fear, anger, hurt, and confusion stand up proudly in our recollections. They come to teach us, even if the lesson is of loss.

She was curious about the white pile on the coffee table. The powdery mound seemed perfect for a pudgy hand to play with. The two-year old toddled up from the floor, across the room, to the low table. Right as she went to stick one extended finger into the mysterious substance, her mother darted at her, smacking her hand.

"Leann! No! You cannot touch that, girl! That's sugar--mommy's sugar. Never ever touch. Okay?" she demanded.

Leann looked up at her wide-eyed mother with an equally shocked expression. She slowly backed away from the table with her eyes downcast.

As Leann walked away she could hear her mother sniffing. She tentatively turned around and saw her mother hunched over the "sugar" which was now in a straight line on the table. She heard her inhale deeply with one finger pressed against a nostril. Leann silently stood and watched her mother as she cradled her own smacked hand in her small arms.

****

When Leann noticed a man and a woman together, she knew she didn't have that anymore; whatever "that" was. Even without the word for "father," she understood that he was missing from her life. There was a faint memory of him from farther back than she could pinpoint, but she sensed she had a father in her life at some point. She wondered where he was, but had no way of asking her mother and therefore, thought little about it.

There were men who visited, but Leann could tell they weren't the same as the dads she would see at the store with their wives and children. Their presence didn't create the same feeling she felt when she watched a man and woman lovingly holding hands on TV.

The men who came to her house were tense and whispering and rarely acknowledged anything beyond her mother. They walked quickly, with hunched shoulders and darting eyes. There were no hugs or greetings when they arrived and their departure was never accompanied by kisses or waves from the front door. The men were blurry in her mind; some with small build, or wide shoulders, maybe a fat belly, or tall and thin. Her mother seemed to know them all, but Leann stayed cautiously in the distance. Even though her mother didn't seem scared of them, Leann sensed she should never get too close to the strangers who came through the house.

****

Leann's belly felt full and hard. She was hungry but didn't want to eat; didn't want to add anything to her cramped insides.

"Oh my God, Leann. What are we going to do? You have

to poop, honey, it's been days. Come on, sit on the potty for mommy."

Leann gripped the sides of the toilet seat so she wouldn't slide backwards into the cold water. She could feel the pressure inside of her, but had no power to force it out. Looking up at her mother pacing above her, Leann felt nervous.

"Honey, what should I do? You gotta get that poopy out. I can't take you to the hospital or nothing. Mommy can't drive right now. What should I do? Can't you push?" she asked, pulling the hair away from her swollen face and bulging eyes.

Her mother resumed her frantic pacing for a few minutes more while Leann continued to clutch the toilet seat and hold up her tiny underwear with her ankles.

Suddenly, her mother darted from the small bathroom. Leann could hear a door open and close. A few minutes later, her mother returned with a smile and a small stick.

"Leann, Mommy has an idea. I'm gonna dig the poopy out, okay? That'll make you feel better," she said as she lifted Leann off the toilet and placed her on the cool tile floor.

Her mother pushed Leann's head forward and inserted the stick. Leann cried out and her small body clenched.

"Come on, Leann, you gotta relax. Let mommy fix you."

After a few more stabs with the stick, her mom seemed to give up. She dropped the stick on the floor and started crying.

"I dunno. Just go to bed. I can't get anything. This is too much right now. I can't handle all this. Just go to bed."

Leann pulled up her underpants carefully and felt a sharp pain inside of her where the stick had cut her. She winced as she took her first steps in the direction of her bedroom. Quietly crying, she made her way past her mother on the couch and up to her bed. Slowly she climbed under the sheet; belly full of pressure and pain, her bottom throbbing from her mother's attempt to help.

****

The car was warm and the straps of her seat made her feel secure, almost embraced. She could feel her eyes getting heavy as her mother pulled into the parking spot. Things faded from her perception as both front doors of the car opened and then slammed shut. She jumped a bit, but easily returned to her cozy slumber.

"Little girl! Are you okay? Hello!"

A man's repeated banging against glass and loud yelling startled Leann awake. She jerked her head to the side where a man stood outside the window of the car. She could feel the cool air now; all the heat from the car had dissipated and she shivered.

Where was her mom? Why was the man so upset?

"Hold on, I'm going to see what's going on," the man tersely stated in response to her puzzled expression.

She suddenly felt tied down in her car seat, cold and alone, but also uncomfortably restricted. Her chest tightened and she felt the tears tickle her eyes before a single drop even fell.

Moments later, her mother appeared. She was pulling at her clothes and wiping her nose in several jerking motions. Close behind her was the angry man who had been at the car window.

"You should be ashamed of yourself! What kind of mother

leaves a baby in the car while she gets high and screws some-one? I mean really, lady, in a gas station bathroom? I'm calling the cops. Your kid ain't safe with you." He ranted from behind her as she unlocked the driver's side door.

"Shut up," she heard her mother mumble as she slid in the front seat. Her head bobbed slightly as she fumbled with her keys and yanked her shirt back in place.

Leann's tears suddenly stopped and she watched with curi-osity to see what would happen next. Would her mom explain where she had been? Was the other man who had been in the car coming out of the gas station to join them? What about the yell-ing man? Would he run after the car if they drove off?

Her mother put the car in reverse and squealed out of the parking lot without another word. The other man who had been in the car earlier was nowhere to be seen.

****

"Hey, I just need you to watch her for a couple of hours. I just have this quick errand and I'll be back. Please, I'll owe you one, Donna!" her mother begged their neighbor.

Donna looked skeptical. She frowned through the screen door and looked down at Leann.

"When will you be back?" she asked.

"By 7 o'clock...at the latest. I promise. Please, I can't take Leann with me."

"I guess, Cindy, but you better be back by 7. I have plans tonight."

"Thank you, thank you, thank you," her mother gushed, "I owe you!"

Leann turned to see her mother jogging to their car and jump in the front passenger seat. She couldn't see the driver, but someone was there because the car quickly revved to life and drove off.

She turned back to Ms. Donna who was still on the other side of the screen door.

"Well, she didn't waste no time," Donna snorted. "Come on in, Leann. You hungry?" She held the door open and stepped to the side as Leann slid in the house against the doorframe.

Leann nodded; she was definitely hungry. Just thinking about food made her thin body shudder. She felt Ms. Donna's hand on her shoulder as she guided her to the kitchen. Leann could smell something cheesy baking in the oven and started to smile at the thought of warm food in her stomach.

Ms. Donna grabbed a potholder and opened the oven. A large pan full of macaroni and cheese took up most of the top rack. Carefully, Ms. Donna pulled it out of the oven and placed it on the stovetop to rest. Leann watched quietly as she got out dishes and silverware. Ms. Donna eventually sent her to get the other children and they all ate until they thought their bellies would bust.

Leann's mom didn't show up at 7pm. Ms. Donna cancelled her plans with a resigned sigh. She put Leann to bed with her other children and watched TV in the living room until her husband came home later that evening.

For several more days, Leann stayed with Ms. Donna and her family and felt cozy, but also uncertain. She couldn't guess where her mother had gone, but she felt content under Ms. Donna's care. Leann had no idea how this adventure would end and wondered if her mother would suddenly appear to swoop her away.

When the doorbell rang the next afternoon, Leann peeked around the living room wall to see a woman in a sweater and dress pants. The new woman sat in a stuffed chair across from Ms. Donna. She wore a badge with a photo of her face on it and nodded robotically as Ms. Donna explained how Leann's mother had asked her to babysit and then never came back.

After they talked for a bit, they both rose from their seats. Ms. Donna called for Leann and explained that the woman with the badge would take her to a family who could watch her until her mom came back.

Leann felt the tears before she understood the sadness that had surfaced. She started crying silently at first, but then a noise rose up in her that she had never heard before. A pained cry spilled out of her and she crumpled onto the floor.

"Come on, Leann, don't be like that," Ms. Donna clucked. She rubbed Leann's head, but seemed to want to stay distant. "Oh my. How does a momma leave her four-year old child?" she asked the woman who was now moving towards the front door.

"It's time to go now, Leann," said the woman, without acknowledging Ms. Donna's question. She must have introduced herself at some point, but Leann's cries were too loud for any extra information to penetrate her awareness.

Together they walked to her car out front. After buckling Leann in a strange car seat, they pulled away from the curb and the only street Leann had ever called home.

Chapter 2

"At the end of the day
All you need is hope and
strength.
Hope that it will get better and
Strength to hold on until it

does."

W alking into the new home made Leann's stomach seize. The front hallway was filled with the musty odor of dirty diapers and sweaty children. There weren't any actual children that she could see, but she could hear their muffled playing in another room. They sounded like a mix of playful and fussy. Leann wasn't sure she wanted to meet them.

Above her, the woman with the badge was talking to a stern-looking couple who seemed to frown and nod at everything that was said. Leann caught wisps of the hushed conversation: "Mother left her with a neighbor for days and hasn't been seen since," "Father's a drug addict and nowhere to be found," "no other family members are qualified to take her at the moment; one grandma is on dialysis and we're looking into the other grandparents," "our office will keep you posted."

Leann stiffened at the reality of being away from her family. Where was her mom? Suddenly, without her consent, something intangible, but very real inside of her hardened and then began to crumble.

As she was guided up the short staircase to the long hallway off the living area and eventually to her new bedroom, Leann felt the rising tide of tears threaten to overtake her vision. When she slowly walked through the doorway of a small room crowded with two single beds, she began to cry. She couldn't contain her sadness, so instead she gave it her full permission to flow. A torrent of emotions gushed out of her and she allowed it to overwhelm her.

Leann collapsed on the unfamiliar floor and let the cries take over her entire body. She felt such a release, lying there sobbing. But under her sadness, she found anger. She didn't want to be here; it wasn't fair. Why was this happening to her? She hit the floor with one foot, then another. Leann slammed a clenched fist against the worn carpet and it felt wild and good. Again she kicked, then punched.

"Hey now!" a voice bellowed over her.

She felt a man's hand on her shoulder. Leann could tell he was trying to calm her, but she wasn't interested in being subdued. She moaned; a low, exhausted cry and went back to thrashing around on the floor. The man turned and left the room, slamming the door on his way out. She heard him stomp down the steps.

Alone in the new space with strange blankets on strange beds that had lumpy pillows that she didn't want to touch, let alone put her face on, Leann felt lost. She curled up on the floor and let the tears drain all the feeling from her body. Her cries had turned into gasps, then hiccups. Since she couldn't stop herself or her body, she tried to relax to get her breathing back to normal.

The door suddenly opened and the stern woman from earlier stood there, looking down at Leann from the doorway.

"That's enough now. Come out for dinner."

Leann followed her down the darkened hallway to the kitchen where a bright florescent light illuminated a long rectangle dining room table. Several children glanced up at her, while others continued eating the food in front of them. Leann sat in the only remaining chair and immediately felt her stomach clench. Despite her exhaustion, she felt tears rising again. Suddenly her whole body began shaking as she tried to contain not only her tears, but her moaning as well.

"Really? Can't you just calm down and eat?" the man asked.

Leann hung her head, hair shielding her face. She had no words, but plenty of pain so she continued to cry. She wished she was back in the bedroom.

"Now you're taking it too far and ruining our dinner. Stop all this nonsense at once!" the man suddenly yelled.

Leann jumped slightly at the sound of his raised voice, but kept her head down.

She felt his large hand grip her arm and lift her out of the chair.

"You're being very disrespectful, young lady," she heard, as he planted her on the floor next to her chair.

She then absorbed the pain from a full-handed slap on her behind and jerked her head up to see all of the children staring at her, some with forks still gripped in their hands.

"Go to your room," she heard him holler.

Without hesitation, Leann retraced her steps back to the bedroom. She held her cries until she quietly closed the door and crawled onto an empty bed. After curling up in the corner of the bed, she let her tears come again and she cried herself to sleep.

Chapter 3

Always remember,

You are loved.

Within a week of being placed in the foster home, a court had granted her grandparents temporary custody of Leann. In a sharp turn of fate, her world went from a stale, musty world of strangers to the warm, cozy home of family.

While Leann's grandfather, Jack, was frustrated with his daughter's drug use, he held nothing but love in his heart for Leann. Jack's second wife, Margo, was equally excited to welcome Leann. They were famous for their family gatherings and "come one, come all" philosophy towards guests.

Instead of an overcrowded bedroom, this time Leann was lead to a sunny bedroom with a single twin bed and a new crib.

"Your little cousin, Joey, lives with us, too. You will both share this room, if that's alright," Margo explained.

Leann walked over to the crib and pressed her face to the cool wooden bars. She could smell the clean powdery scent of her little cousin and smiled when she realized he was curled up in the corner, sleeping.

She looked up at her grandmother and smiled broadly.

"You two are gonna get along just fine," she heard Margo whisper.

Leann quickly realized she could relax and smile again, so she did. At family gatherings and holidays, she allowed her cousins and other relatives to include her in games and silly conversations. Leann was learning what "normal" meant for the first time.

Her grandfather worked as a truck driver and had fun showing Leann his tractor-trailer. Leann would climb up the side and crawl onto the driver's seat, bouncing on the cushioned seat with both arms outstretched to jerk the massive steering wheel left and right.

"Wanna try the horn, Leann?" he always asked, once she got tired of the driving.

"Yes, yes, yes!" Leann would squeal as she crawled up to a kneeling position.

Invariably she'd jump as soon as she pulled the cord looped from the ceiling that made the horn blast. Then she giggled, so much giggling after that.

Leann would then pretend to be tired and climb through the two front seats to the back area that included a cozy mattress with blankets. She'd curl up for a few minutes and act like she was asleep.

"Now I never heard such silly snoring in all my life, Leann," her grandfather teased as he watched her from the doorframe. Leann would erupt in more giggles and open her eyes, smiling down at him from her snug perch.

****

On one particularly snowy afternoon, Leann sat curled up on the couch with a book when her grandfather came over and sat next to her.

"Honey, your mommy wants to see you again. I know it's been a long time, but she had to go away to a place… like a big girl time out. She wants you to visit her because she will be there for a while."

Leann looked up from her picture book and smiled. She remembered her mother and was happy to hear news about her.

"Let's put on your coat and pay her a visit, okay?" Her grandfather asked with a nodding smile.

Leann jumped up from her nook on the couch and tugged her red coat off the hook by the front door. While she pushed her arms into each sleeve, she also wiggled her toes into her snow boots.

"Alright, speedy girl. Wait for me!" Jack chuckled as he pushed up from the couch and retrieved his coat from the front hall closet.

Holding her small hand in his, he opened the front door to the white December afternoon and they walked over to his Buick parked in the driveway.

At the prison, Leann continued to hold her grandfather's hand. He guided her through the security checks until they reached the family meeting area. Leann hesitated when she saw all of the round tables with sets of strangers circled around each one. Her grandfather steered her to an empty one near a row of vending machines.

"Let's sit here, Leann. How about a soda and a little snack?" he whispered pointing a finger towards the machines.

Leann's eyes widened as she thought of the possibilities, but then she quickly decided on a Sprite and a bag of potato chips. She nibbled and sipped on her treats while they waited for whatever would happen next.

By the time she was licking the last salt from her finger-tips, Leann noticed some guards coming in the room with arms full of wrapped presents. Each one was marked "boy" or "girl" and they seemed to be for the children around the tables. Leann wiggled on the hard metal bench wondering if she would receive one of the "girl" gifts.

Outside the glass doors, Leann recognized a woman who was lined up with other inmates. They were all wearing the same color tops and bottoms. One at time, they walked up to the doorway and said something to a guard who then either handed them a boy or girl gift. When the familiar-looking woman got to the doorway she took a present and looked over at Leann with a teary smile. Leann recognized her mother and returned the smile without hesitation.

"Whoa, you sure got big, Leann!" she said, sitting down across from Leann and her grandfather.

"Hey there, Cindy," Leann's grandfather said politely, "How are you holding up?"

"Oh, I'm fine. Thanks so much for bringing her by, Dad. I can't believe how different she looks. It hasn't been but a few weeks."

"Well, she's been through a lot, you know. Leann's doing real well; sharing a room with little Joey and all." Her grandfather was nodding while talking, as if to assure her mother that she knew all this but had just forgotten.

"Joey? Oh, because Angie is in jail…that's right. You're going to have him for a while since she'll be locked up for so long. Actually, I'm glad they let you have Leann, too. I know how Social Services can be about kids sharing a room."

Cindy looked deep into her father's eyes and continued, "I'm so grateful that you're doing this for me, Dad. Angie and I are going to get our shit together after this. I promise."

Leann saw her grandfather raise his eyebrow and suppress a chuckle knowing that his daughters often made promises they couldn't keep.

He changed the subject.

"So what do you have there?" He asked, nodding towards the wrapped gift.

"Oh, yeah! Leann, here's a Christmas gift for you, baby!" Her mother exclaimed, pushing the gift across the buffed metal table until it was directly in front of Leann's nose.

Leann popped up from her seated position and stood on her bench. She quickly unwrapped a large doll baby with beady eyes that stared at her emotionless. Leann instantly loved her long brown hair and began to pull at the cardboard container to get the doll out.

"Hold on, Leann, let me help you with that," her grandfather insisted.

"Leann, come over to Mommy and let me hold you." Her mother grabbed Leann's hand lovingly and pulled her around the table.

"I miss you so much, baby girl!" she said through tears, kisses, and firm hugs.

Leann didn't know how to feel; she missed her mother and couldn't understand how she was living in this place instead of coming home.

"I made some real bad mistakes, hon. Mommy's gonna have to stay in here for a little while, but I'll come home soon. When I get out of here, Leann, I'm gonna take you to the beach, the park, and the pool. Where do you want me to take you, huh?"

Leann could somewhat hear her mother from under her heavy embrace, and attempted a muffled reply.

"Let the girl breathe, Cindy!" Leann heard her grandfather say.

Her mother loosened her grip and handed Leann the newly opened doll baby. Leann climbed up onto the bench next to her mother and played with the doll's long hair and fancy dress while her mother and grandfather continued their conversation.

"So we've heard from Roger. He's been dating a real nice lady. Think she's trying to straighten him out. He looks good."

Leann felt her mother's body stiffen next to her.

"As long as he knows that Leann is my child and he can't just take her back. I don't want any other woman around her, either. I don't know why he comes by your place anyway."

Again her grandfather smiled and said nothing.

They stayed at the round table for a while longer until the guards came by each table and tapped anyone wearing a jumpsuit. The identically dressed adults gave final kisses and hugs before filing back out of the doorway they had entered. Leann waved to her mother as she walked out of sight.

On the drive home Leann felt an ache in her stomach. Seeing her mother was relief, but it also triggered her loneliness. Even though she was young, she felt the emptiness of losing her home and her only parent.

Leann could feel her grandfather's eyes on her as he drove. Looking up at him and locking in on his smiling gaze, she was instantly calmed.

"It's gonna be hard, Leann," he said, nodding. "But you know we love you and we'll take good care of you till your mom can get herself better. You two will be back together someday."

Leann nodded, but said nothing.

****

Life settled into a comfortable routine with her grandparents over the next few months. She loved helping them with the parties they frequently held at their house. It was fun to be in a happy house.

One morning as Leann read her favorite Dr. Seuss book in bed, her grandfather stepped into her room,

"You remember we have a party to get ready for, right?" he asked, his voice lighter than normal.

Leann jerked her head up and looked at him, "We do?"

"Yep, we always have a Memorial Day party and this year will beat 'em all." Jack winked at Leann and she giggled.

"We are inviting all grandma's family, whoever they wanna bring, and we'll invite the neighbors so they can't fuss cuz we're having so much fun without them!"

Leann giggled again. She loved the cookouts she'd attended at her grandparents' house. She had vague memories of a smoky grill, constant music and conversation, the water-wings she wore in the above-ground pool, and all the cousins who would chase her around the big grassy lawn.

Suddenly she sat up straight in her bed and smiled.

"Can I have root beer at the party?" she asked hopefully.

"Sure can!" Jack replied, "How many hotdogs do you think you'll eat? You know I make the best hotdogs around."

"I'm gonna eat ten!" Leann declared.

"Ten hot dogs?! Leann, you're gonna turn into a hot dog if you do that!" Jack teased.

Leann burst into laughter at the thought. She eventually rested her head against the pile of pillows and realized how happy she was at that moment. Her entire body was relaxed and content.

****

Life passed by in a new type of normal. Leann started school with fresh shoes and brand new clothes. She'd picked out her backpack and TrapperKeeper. On the first day of school, she took pictures with baby Joey out front before she boarded the school bus. Her teacher was nice enough and schoolwork was interesting. The routine of life with her grandparents was calm and predictable. Leann felt at ease in the safety of their care.

Christmas the next year brought Margo's family pouring back into the house. Leann was excited to see all of her cousins and she stood, nose pressed against the cool window, to watch for their cars to arrive. She wore her new red velvet dress and shiny black strap shoes with her long hair braided down the back of her neck.

Leann announced each family as their cars pulled up to the front curb. She'd wait until they were about to reach the front door and then run to swing the door wide open. She welcomed everyone with, "Merry Christmas!" and a grin that was missing a tooth or two.

Everyone who walked through the doorway reached down to hug Leann or pat her on the head as they peeled off coats and slipped off snowy shoes. The aunts and uncles headed downstairs to Grandpa Jack at the bar, where he was handing out cocktails, or to the kitchen to help Margo finish the cooking in the kitchen.

Leann would race around the house with the cousins and baby Joey until the next car pulled up out front. They'd also stop their running on occasion to grab a mouthful of Chex Mix or a square of cheese and then return to their gleeful pursuits.

Jack shook his head and smiled from his post at the bar. He took a sip of his Screwdriver and scanned the room. Everyone was eating from his or her plate of home-cooked food. Margo's recipes were famous and most of the family waited for gatherings to have the treats, not daring to recreate it on their own.

The holiday evening passed in cozy blur and Leann eventually collapsed in bed after an exhausting and exhilarating visit with cousins.

****

When warmer weather came around again, so did Leann's father. At first she assumed he was a family friend, but her grandfather quickly cleared up her misunderstanding.

"Leann, come here, darling," he waved to her with his long metal spatula from the grill.

She obediently walked over to the grilling area.

"Leann, this is your father and I invited him today because he's been asking to see you."

Her head cocked to the right as she considered this news and then Leann shifted her gaze to the new man standing next to the grill. He held a beer in one hand and had a gentle smile. Leann felt a connection to him, even though she struggled with the idea that this stranger was her father.

"It's been a long time since I've seen you, Leann. You would've been too little to remember the last time we were together."

He waited while she processed this information; he *had* been in her life. A long time ago, when she was a baby like Joey, she had a dad. She imagined herself as a baby in his arms for a moment, and then looked back to him standing beside her grandfather. He was still smiling slightly. Leann could sense that he didn't want to rush her and she was grateful that he wasn't trying to hug her or be too friendly.

"I was just telling Jack, uhh, your grandfather, that I'm moving into a townhouse nearby. If it's okay with you, I'll stop by and say hi from time to time."

Jack stood off to the side flipping burgers, nodding silent support as the Leann's father talked.

"Okay," Leann quietly responded. She wasn't sure what else to say. She wasn't uncomfortable, but she didn't feel like talking much more with this new man. She'd have to think about this new development some more when he wasn't standing right in front of her.

Her grandfather could sense her awkwardness, "Go play with your cousins, Leann, and we'll talk more with your daddy later."

Leann nodded, smiled meekly up at Roger, the man who was her long-lost father, and ran off towards the children in the pool.

****

Over the next six months, Jack invited Roger to every family gathering and Leann grew more comfortable talking with him. She heard stories about his childhood, his new townhouse, and a woman he was dating named Elaine.

"How'd you meet this new lady?" Margo asked during one of Roger's visits. Jack, sipping on his Screwdriver, sat next to Leann on the picnic bench to hear the story.

"Well, you know I love bowling," Roger began, "One night I saw this lady and she just seemed so together. I don't know how to explain it, but she was different from the other ladies I've dated."

Jack chuckled, but didn't interrupt.

"She smiled at me and I decided to talk to her. Turns out she is pretty religious and she won't tolerate any nonsense. I liked how tough she was. I ended up telling her about my troubles in the past," Roger paused and glanced over to Leann, "and she didn't judge me at all. She seemed to understand how hard it is to stay clean." Roger seemed embarrassed for a moment and took a swig of his beer.

"Anyway," he continued, "she's been real supportive, but also tough. She doesn't put up with any of my excuses and that's really what I like about her."

"That's great, dear," Margo said patiently, "Tell us more about her family."

"Actually she had a very rough childhood and got out of her house with the help of this great guy, Denny. He's real sweet; an older fellow. He took her in and they got married. I know it sounds crazy, Elaine was super young, but it worked for them, even though he's like 20 years older."

"Oh my," Margo interrupted, "how are you two together then?"

"Well, it's a crazy situation, I know, but Denny is old and pretty sick right now. Probably gonna die soon. Anyhow, he just wants Elaine to move on because she has a lot of life left. He likes me, so I've kind of got his blessing and all."

Roger paused to let everyone absorb the details of his new relationship.

"Can't say I've heard of anything like this before," Jack finally broke the silence, "but if you all are happy and this guy Denny is okay with it, then I guess it's good."

Roger's shoulders relaxed as he exhaled. It was obvious he valued Jack's opinion. Roger turned his eyes to Margo.

Margo smiled slightly and nodded, "Definitely a unique situation."

Leann looked from one adult to another trying to understand their conversation.

"You thinking you'll bring her here sometime? She's welcome to come with you to our next cookout," Margo added.

"Thanks, Margo," Roger replied, "I appreciate that. It'd be nice for you guys to meet her. Is that okay with you, Leann?"

All eyes turned to Leann and she felt her face redden.

"Uh, yes, that's okay with me."

"Great," Roger said sitting up straighter, "I think this is gonna be a great thing for us." He nodded toward Leann. "We can hang out and see if we all get along. It'll be nice."

Leann forced an uneasy smile. A new woman; a flash of her

mother's jealous face filled her mind. She continued smiling, but understood that things were shifting in ways she couldn't understand yet. She held her lips in a grin, but her stomach clenched slightly.

Chapter 4

Never Forget 3 Types of People in Your Life

1. Those who helped you in your difficult times
2. Those who left you in your difficult times
3. Those who put you in your difficult times

Meeting Elaine felt like a repeat of the afternoon Leann met her father. During a particularly hot barbeque at her grandparents' house, Leann saw her father across the backyard. She was bobbing up and down in the pool and caught intermittent glimpses of him talking with her grandfather at the grill. Not that this was note-worthy, her father regularly attended the cookouts now. Leann was used to his presence and would often sit with him when she got around to eating a hot dog or burger. She liked that he was easy to be around: very kind and not pushy at all.

Today Leann felt like something was off, different. In the next moment she noticed her grandmother was with a new woman and they were both walking towards the men at the grill. As she popped in and out of the water, Leann realized that her dad was introducing the woman to her grandfather.

"That's the girlfriend," Leann muttered to herself.

She suddenly felt all the adult eyes shift in her direction. Like before, her grandfather waved her over to the gathering by the grill.

Leann swam over to the edge of the pool and climbed out. She grabbed her new pink towel and tried not to think about her mother. Leann knew she wouldn't want a new woman around, but if *her* father was inviting her over, what could Leann do? She had to be respectful to her grandfather.

Still wrapped in her towel, Leann walked through the grass in her bare feet to the smoking grill and the four adults. They were all smiling and laughing politely until Leann was right next to her grandfather.

"Hey, there!" Jack grinned. "Leann, this is Miss Elaine. She and your dad are getting really close so he thought he'd bring her over so you could meet her."

"I think you two will really hit it off," her dad added.

Leann looked from her grandfather to her father and then finally to the new woman. Elaine looked friendly with her nervous smile and outstretched hand. She squatted down to be at eye level with Leann.

Leann pulled her hand out from under her towel and shook Elaine's hand.

"It's nice to meet you, Leann. I hope we can get to know each other better."

Leann nodded silently and wondered what she was supposed to say. Elaine didn't seem to expect much of a reply and slowly stood up and went back to standing next to Roger. She was still smiling in Leann's direction, but all the adults seemed to be giving Leann some space to take in this new situation.

The rest of the day turned out to be a blur of eating, playing, and napping poolside. Music and laughter mingled with splashing and the smell of grilling. It was a perfect, peaceful day.

****

Elaine and Roger became regular guests at the cookouts that summer. They would often bring a case of beer or a salad to share with everyone. Leann quickly grew used to seeing them together and even looked forward to sitting with both of them at a picnic table while she ate.

At one particular cookout, Leann saw her dad and Elaine arrive with a shopping bag. For some reason, she instantly knew the contents were for her. With an expectant grin, she skipped over to them as they walked across the back patio.

"Hey there, Leann!" Elaine exclaimed. "We went shopping for you, Missy!"

"Yeah! What did you get me?" Leann asked as they all sat down on a lounge chair.

"Oh you'll see!" Elaine replied. "I hope you like what we picked out."

Leann opened the bag and pulled out sundress after sundress, a new bathing suit, and some cool glitter sunglasses. Her cheeks ached from her wide grin.

"There are some cute flip-flops in there, too, honey," her dad finally chimed in.

Leann found the new sandals and jumped up to do a happy dance.

"Well," Elaine chuckled, "I guess we did good!"

"Can I go try some of these on now?" Leann asked.

"Of course!" they both replied.

Leann tore into the house and ran through the kitchen to her bedroom to try on her new clothes. When she came downstairs she pretended to be a fashion model and Roger, Elaine, and her grandparents all clapped and whistled for her.

"Leann if you can sit still over here, I'll do a really pretty braid in your hair. Then you'll really look like a fancy girl," Elaine offered.

As Leann raced back to the lounge chair for her new hairdo, her grandfather clapped Roger on the back.

"I think this gal may be the best move you've made, Roger"

Roger nodded, grinning.

"I love my daughter, but she has a lot going on," Jack conceded. "Plus, I think you two brought out the devil in one another."

"Yeah, I feel bad that Cindy can't be here for Leann right now, but I'd like to do my part." Jack nodded and Roger continued, "Elaine really has a plan for us, too. She and I are gonna buy a place together and see if we can make a home for Leann."

Leann concentrated on sitting still while Elaine braided her hair, but she noticed her grandfather tense up out of the corner of her eye.

"Not right now, of course," Roger added. "We need to get ourselves settled and figure out how all this custody stuff works. But we would like to help out with her more and maybe take her out so she can get to know us better."

Leann moved slightly to glimpse her grandfather's expression. He was nodding, but not smiling.

"Yes, I guess that makes sense," he finally muttered.

"Maybe once a week for now," Roger offered.

"Sounds fine. It makes me feel good that you're getting your life back together and making your daughter a priority. I know, on some level, that Cindy would appreciate that, too."

Both men chuckled at the thought of Cindy approving these new developments.

"I'm not so sure about that, but I'm gonna continue on this path. It's good for me to be clean and working. Elaine has really been hard on me, but that's what I need."

"You're welcome, Roger," Elaine chimed in with a chuckle

from the lounge chair.

****

After that party, Elaine and Roger would visit the house more often and take Leann on brief outings. Leann loved the special time on her own with them, away from her baby cousin.

Eventually Elaine would take Leann out for girl-time; they'd go shopping or to the movies. Elaine always asked Leann what she was in the mood for and then they'd set out on their day trip.

Leann loved their visits to Chuck E Cheese or the photo center at Sears. She felt light and happy with a young mother-figure in her life. Their lunches at restaurants and girl-time made Leann excited for the day when she could move in with them.

One day over french fries and milkshakes, Elaine explained that they were going to go to court so that Leann could live with them in their new place.

"Your mom will be in the courtroom and I know you haven't seen her in a while. I just don't want you to be surprised."

Leann nodded and thought about the two women in the same room. It made her squirm a bit, but if Leann had to choose, she realized she would prefer to move in with her dad and Elaine.

****

A few weeks later, everything happened as Elaine had described: the courtroom was an intimidating place and Leann's mother was brought in with shackles around her wrists and ankles. They briefly made eye contact, but her mom was at the front of the courtroom and Leann was sitting in the back, snug between her grandparents.

The judge read through the case and summarily gave custody to the mother of the child.

The courtroom collectively gasped and the judge looked up, startled.

"Your Honor, we are asking that you grant the father custody since his ex-wife is currently incarcerated."

The judge seemed to finally take stock of the situation and looked over to where Cindy sat in her jumpsuit and handcuffs.

"Oh my. I'm...you're right. I misspoke," he stammered. "I hereby grant custody to the father...Mr. Roger Brown"

Everyone exhaled and Leann felt her grandfather kiss her on the top of her head.

Things were going to be different now: a new home, a new set of parents, and a new lifestyle. Leann felt happy and content. Things were working out better all the time.

Chapter 5

"Someday everything will make perfect sense. So for now, laugh at the confusion, smile through the tears, and keep reminding yourself that everything happens for a reason."

L eann moved into the new house and quickly got used to being an only child again. Because Elaine told her all of the time, Leann knew that Roger and Elaine couldn't have any children. It didn't bother Leann to be the only child; she loved the attention and the girl-time she had with Elaine.

They sometimes visited Dennis, Elaine's older, sick husband, who sat quietly propped up in his bed all day. Leann was fascinated by Dennis' favorite treat: large round lollipops that had a worm at the center.

"Oh, those are called tequila pops, Leann," Elaine explained one day, "they're just for grown-ups."

Leann let out a relieved sigh, but continued to watch in fascination as Dennis licked his way to the center.

She later overheard her dad and Elaine discussing how she was still married to Dennis, which didn't seem to bother her father. Apparently he was content with things the way they were: the three of them building a life together with Dennis lingering in the background.

Elaine slipped into the role of mother quite easily. She signed up to be the first grade room mother for Leann's class and would impress everyone with her cupcakes and decorating skills. Friends would come over to play at their house because Leann had all of the coolest new toys and didn't mind sharing her new things with others.

One afternoon while Leann was cleaning up after a play

date, she called to Elaine from the living room.

"Mom, can I have a snack?"

The silence that followed Leann's verbal slip lingered in the air until Elaine came to the doorway. Leann could feel her cheeks burning.

"It's okay, Leann, you can call me Mom. Really, honey, it's fine."

Leann exhaled and went back to putting away her toys. She hadn't meant to say "mom," but now that it was over, she didn't want to go back to calling her Elaine.

Leann thought briefly of her mother in prison and winced. She wouldn't mind, Leann told herself. Every girl deserved a mother who was actually around, she further reasoned. On the rare occasions that Leann did visit her mother, she would promise to call Leann, but would never actually follow through. Leann knew that her mother would send letters to her from time to time, but Elaine had told her it was better if she didn't read them. Elaine worried the letters would upset Leann. On some level Leann appreciated how Elaine protected her, but there was still an ache for a maternal figure in her life. Elaine was perfectly positioned to be her mother now; it just felt like a natural shift.

"Let me braid your hair, sweetie," Elaine offered one morning.

"Okay!" Leann replied. She quickly finished getting dressed and followed Elaine down to the kitchen.

"I made you a Toaster Strudel for breakfast, do you want to drizzle the icing?"

"Yes, yes, I love doing that," Leann answered, jumping in place.

"Alright, nice and easy, Missy. Good…" Elaine stood over Leann as she carefully zig-zagged the white icing on the sizzling pastry. She gave Leann's shoulder a loving squeeze as she finished. "Now you sit down at the table and eat that while I braid your pretty hair."

Leann skipped over to the table and then nibbled away at her breakfast as Elaine gently brushed Leann's hair. Dividing her hair into three strands, Elaine gently braided Leann's two pigtails until they fell neatly down each side of her back.

"Thank you!" Leann exclaimed as she turned her head left and right. Her braids bounced against her shoulders and Leann smiled broadly.

"You look real pretty, Leann. It's time for school now, but I want you to think about what we should buy for everybody in your class for Valentine's Day."

"Oh!" Leann's eyes widened.

"Think we should go over to Kmart after school and see what they've got?"

"Yes, yes, yes!" Leann squealed. "I wanna get everyone those cards that you stick a lollipop through."

"Alright," Elaine chuckled. "Be a good girl at school today and we'll head over there when you get home this afternoon. Maybe we'll even get a snack while we're out," she added, with a wink.

Leann smiled in response and slipped on her coat and book bag.

"Thanks for being such a great mom," Leann said, hugging Elaine's waist. Leann didn't feel guilty saying it. She just felt grateful she was so loved.

****

Life suddenly changed when Elaine announced that she was pregnant.

Having babies was supposed to be impossible for Elaine so the pregnancy was labeled a miracle for anyone who asked.

Roger was just as shocked as anyone when the doctor slapped him on the back in congratulations for a job well done. The doctor repeated that he couldn't believe Elaine was able to carry a baby. Roger's face in the office that day mirrored the doctor's surprise.

Another shift happened shortly after that doctor's visit. It was decided that they would move out of their town home and into a detached house. Roger had to promise that he would put on a two-story addition to expand the small house before Elaine would agree with the move. Over the next few months, Roger called in favors from all of his buddies in the construction industry. One by one, they'd show up to clear the foundation, put up the framing, hang electrical wiring, and then Roger would install the HVAC. As Elaine's belly grew, so did their house. By the time the baby was born, their home was almost double its original size.

To outsiders, these steps symbolized a positive change for the family. Furthermore, Leann was excited at the idea of helping with a baby again and loved watching all of the new space being created on their house. Meanwhile, Roger was dutifully working and providing for his family. He secretly wished the miracle baby was a son. His hopes came true when Caleb was born that spring.

Elaine was an older mother and the birth seemed to take a lot out of her. Her recovery was slow and required many additional hands to help with the baby, clean the house, and cook meals. Leann did her best to ease the workload while also staying out of the way.

During quiet moments, Leann would often think about her new little brother. The house had changed with his arrival and Leann would look at him asleep in his crib with wonder; so many shifts just because of this little person.

She also worried about Elaine; things felt strained between them since Caleb was born. They never went out together anymore, and Elaine also seemed irritated if Leann left the house with her father. She would become irate, and scream at Roger if he tried to take Leann to the corner store or out on an errand. Roger, who seemed more tired than he used to, would leave alone instead of putting up a fight.

Leann didn't mind helping with baby Caleb, but Elaine would often demand that she run bottles to the crib early in the morning when she claimed she was too fatigued to get out of bed. After a few weeks, helping with the baby wasn't fun anymore; it felt like a chore. Leann noticed that she really looked forward to school each day. She thrived in the classroom and she relished the break from her monotonous life at home.

Things were definitely changing and Leann wasn't sure how

she fit in to the new family dynamic. Her father and Elaine had recently gone to the courthouse to get officially married. They celebrated with Leann by bringing her a cupcake to school while they were still dressed up in their wedding attire. It seemed a little strange, but nothing surprised Leann any more.

She wondered if things would finally settle into a peaceful balance again once Caleb was a little older and Elaine had fully recovered from her pregnancy.

Her theory would never be tested, because within the year, Elaine was pregnant again.

Chapter 6

"You own everything that
happened to you.
Tell your stories.
If people wanted you to write
warmly about them, they

should've behaved better."

The rain was pouring outside, as Leann got dressed for the 100th day of school in her 3rd grade year. She hummed to herself as she picked out her outfit and made her bed. When she heard Elaine holler from the front hallway, she ran from her room and down the stairs. Elaine was at the bottom of the stairs holding Caleb on her hip beside her growing belly. For some reason she looked annoyed with Leann as she approached.

"Do you understand you are so late for school that you don't have time for breakfast?" she sneered.

Leann felt confused, but didn't argue. She was hungry and thought about the morning ahead with a growling stomach. "I put your lunch box in your book bag and here's your rain-coat," Elaine huffed.

Leann took the book bag and placed it between her feet while she slipped on her raincoat. She then strapped on her book bag and headed out into the rain.

Even though she heard the front door close behind her, Leann had a feeling that Elaine was still watching her from the front of the house as she walked to the street. The rain was still pounding down on her and Leann could tell her shoes were fill-ing with water because her socks were already soaked.

When Leann got to the corner where she crossed to meet her friend, Sarah, she saw that Sarah's mom was warming up the car. Leann sighed with relief as they both waved her over to them.

"Hurry, honey, get in!" Sarah's mom shouted.

Leann hustled towards them and slid in the back seat of the

car. The two girls smiled at one another, both grateful to be in the cozy car and out of the downpour. On the way to school, Leann pulled out the thin cheese sandwich she had in her lunch box and carefully split it in half. She slowly chewed one half during the car ride and saved the other half for her lunch.

The school day started off normally, but during reading time Leann was called to the front office.

"Please have Leann bring all of her belongings with her," the secretary requested.

Confused, Leann gathered her things and walked to the front office. She saw Elaine and the baby stroller waiting for her in the front foyer. Leann scrunched her eyebrows wondering if she'd forgotten a dentist appointment or something.

"Come on, Leann, we're going home," Elaine muttered.

Leann followed her to the car and sat in silence in the back seat next to Caleb. When they got in house, Elaine ordered Leann up to her room. Leann could hear Elaine stomping around the kitchen and then up the stairs towards her bedroom.

The door swung open and Elaine filled the frame with her hands on her hips.

"Who told you that you could get a ride to school?" Elaine hissed.

"What do you mean?" Leann's mind was racing. "Do you mean Sarah? Sarah's mom said she'd take me because it was raining," Leann replied in a steady voice, confident that this would clear up the misunderstanding and calm Elaine down.

"Don't you dare sass me, Leann! I will not have it. I cannot believe you think you can do what you want all the time. You're a child; I'm the grown-up. You need to get that straight in your head."

Leann felt disoriented and went to explain, again, that she and Sarah walked to school together every single day. As she went to speak, a slash of pain flamed up on her cheek. The breath constricted in her chest and she stumbled backwards onto her bed.

"There you go, trying to sass me again!" Elaine interrupted Leann's thoughts, her voice rising. "I can see you're thinking about the next smartass thing you're gonna say." Leann now noticed that Elaine was holding a wooden spoon in her right hand.

"I'm sorry, sorry…" Leann stuttered.

"Oh, yeah? You're gonna be sorry when I'm done with you," Elaine was now screaming as she grabbed a chunk of Leann's hair with one hand and hit her again with the other hand.

"I'm not putting up with this shit. Not in my house. I'm gonna have too many children to take care of to worry about this ridiculous stuff!" Elaine yelled as she released Leann's hair and pushed her on the bed. For a moment, Elaine paused to catch her breath and rub her growing belly as if it were bothering her.

In the next moment, she lunged for Leann.

Leann instinctively rolled over on the bed to her stomach to shield her face. Elaine continued smacking Leann as she lay face down, holding her with one hand and beating her with a new metal spatula since the wooden spoon had split in half. Tears filled Leann's eyes as she felt the cuts split open her back. She could hear Elaine cursing at her with each blow.

"Get up and put on your pajamas. You ain't going nowhere.

You're staying here to think about what you've done," Elaine was now out of breath again as she threw Leann's red and black flannel nightgown at her on the bed.

Leann heard the door slam and Elaine's receding footsteps. Painfully she slid to the edge of her bed and carefully stood up. Her entire body was throbbing from welts that she could feel rising all over her. She reached a shaking hand towards the nightgown and pulled it towards her. With aching muscles, she managed to pull off her clothes, now streaked with blood. She gingerly put her nightgown over her head and let it fall down her body.

With one hand, Leann pulled down the sheets and comforter and crawled back in bed. Then, closing her eyes, she allowed the tears to flow. She fell asleep and stayed under her covers through the rest of the day. Dinner came and went, but Leann could not rise from her bed.

The next morning, she woke up with aching muscles, but found the strength to crawl off the bed when she heard Elaine calling to her from the kitchen.

Leann went through her morning routine and made her bed and pulled clean clothes from her drawer. When she went to pull off her flannel nightgown, she felt a pulling of her skin. She couldn't understand what was causing the acute pain, so she continued pulling her arms and head through the openings. Only after she pulled the nightgown completely over her head, did Leann realize she was ripping new scabs off her back. The blood from the cuts on her body had soaked into the nightgown and hardened overnight. When she pulled off her nightgown, she reopened all of her wounds.

Leann felt new tears forming in her eyes, but continued getting dressed before Elaine felt compelled to come upstairs to get her. She gently pulled her clothes on over the fresh sores and walked downstairs.

Elaine was waiting for her at the bottom of the stairs.

"Hurry up and get some breakfast. You need to leave in a few minutes." Elaine looked emotionless as she turned and returned to the kitchen.

"Okay," Leann muttered, mostly to herself. She wondered if Elaine was going to say anything about hitting her the day before. On some, deeper level, she knew that Elaine would never apologize or explain her actions.

"Let's go, Leann!" Elaine called from the kitchen.

Later that day, after Leann had several classes and lunch, she couldn't shake the feeling of sadness that enveloped her.

"What's wrong, Leann?" her friend Sarah asked as they walked to PE class.

"I'm just sore from my punishment yesterday," Leann replied, slightly surprised she answered so honestly.

"Punishment? What did you do?" Sarah questioned.

"I guess I wasn't supposed to go in the car with you yesterday."

"But it was raining really hard! Why weren't you allowed to ride with us?" Sarah looked completely baffled.

"I don't know," Leann paused, "I really don't understand why she got so mad."

"Who? Your stepmom? Is that why you left class yesterday?" Sarah asked.

"Yes, she came and got me and when we got home she hit me over and over again. I have cuts on my back now."

"You do?" Sarah's voice had a nervous edge to it now.

"Yep, look," Leann replied. She paused in the hallway and lifted the back of her shirt for Sarah to see.

"Oh my god, Leann!" Sarah's hand went to her mouth. "That's really, really bad. I'm so sorry that happened because we gave you a ride to school."

Leann shrugged. She didn't understand how it all connected either. Until the baby came, Elaine was loving and patient with Leann. Now she was unpredictable and moody. Leann felt tense even thinking about Elaine and dreaded the thought of returning home while her father was still at work.

The rest of the school day was uneventful and Leann eventually ended up back at home. She could feel a raised level of tension as soon as she walked through the door.

"Leann, I hope you understand that *anything* that happens in this house stays in this house," Elaine hissed. She seemed to appear out of nowhere.

"Uh, yes. I guess."

"No guessing necessary. You don't go talking about me or this family to anyone. No one. What happens in this house, stays in this house. Bottom line."

Elaine walked off before Leann could completely process what she had said. She had no idea why Elaine would be at the door waiting to tell her that as soon as she walked in.

Within an hour, Leann realized why Elaine had been so insistent. Two people in business suits, wearing badges, appeared at the front door. Elaine greeted them warmly, while acting confused about their arrival.

"I have no idea why you're here, but I'm sure we can clear up any misunderstanding. You folks want some iced tea?" Elaine offered with a smile.

Both visitors glanced over to Leann, who was standing in the doorframe of the kitchen. She had no idea what was happening, but she kept hearing Elaine in her mind saying, "What happens in this house, stays in this house," over and over again.

The rest of their visit went by in a haze: questions that were directed at Leann which Elaine would quickly answer, notes being taken by the officials, and glances back and forth between all the adults. Then Elaine explaining how Leann had fallen down the stairs and scratched up her back, and Leann weakly lifting her shirt with an understanding that it wouldn't make a difference. They believed Elaine. The officials eventually left and walked out to their car.

Elaine and Leann stood on the porch together as the car backed out of the driveway. Elaine took her hand off of Leann's shoulder once they had completely pulled away from the house. She then turned and went in the house and closed the door in Leann's face.

Later that night, Leann fell asleep as she listened to Elaine screaming at Roger. She was retelling the events of the day and the horrible lies Leann had told classmates at school. Every so often Leann could hear a pause for what she assumed was a question from her father, and then Elaine would start screaming again about how terrible Leann had been. Her father didn't argue for long and then the house was quiet.

****

After the next beating for talking back or being disobedient or some other violation Leann didn't understand, she decided to confide in her father and showed him her bruises. He looked pained and stroked her hair nervously.

The yelling lasted longer that evening.

But the next day Leann was punished even more severely because she had complained to her father. She quickly learned to keep her pain to herself. She didn't dare mention her punishments to anyone again.

By the time Leann started 4th grade and had two younger brothers at home, she had learned how to stay away from Elaine. She would often play off to the side with her toys, far away from Elaine.

One afternoon, Elaine grew annoyed with Leann and her toys and told her to go outside and pick up all of the sticks from the yard.

"All of the sticks?" Leann questioned.

"Yeah, do you have a problem? We all help out around here. Get out there and do as you're told."

Elaine handed Leann a handful of plastic grocery bags and pushed her out the door. Before Leann stood an expansive yard filled with tall oak trees. It was hard to see a spot on the lawn that didn't have a stick or a twig. Leann looked around and felt her shoulders fall. Slowly, she bent down and picked up a stick and put it in the bag.

After several hours, Leann was exhausted, but satisfied with her efforts. She took a deep breath and headed back inside the house after placing the last bag of sticks on the pile she had made near the trash cans.

"What are you doing back in here already?" Elaine sneered, turning from her soap operas.

Leann paused as she walked through the living room.

"I'm done. I picked up every stick outside."

Elaine huffed as she pulled herself off the couch and walked towards the door. Leann froze when Elaine put her hand on the door knob to go outside.

"Are you kidding me, Leann?" Elaine questioned, waving her arms in front of her. "There are sticks all over the place. What have you been doing all this time? Playing around?"

Leann looked outside past Elaine and could only see the tiniest twigs still remaining. She avoided Elaine's eyes as she stormed back into the house. "I'm so sick of you! You're going to end up in jail like your mom. You're going to flip burgers for living. Like mother, like daughter."

Leann couldn't understand what was happening or why Elaine was so mad, but she knew what would happen next.

Elaine grabbed a spatula from the kitchen counter and started beating Leann across the head, arms, and back. She continued to scream at her about how useless she was and how she'd end up just like her mother: in jail.

Once she grew tired, Elaine pushed Leann out of the room and returned to her soap operas. Leann crawled up the stairs to her room and crawled under the blankets.

****

When Leann had reached her 9th birthday, she started to grow rapidly and always felt hungry. Her relationship with her step-mother was cold and indifferent most days, then an unexpected tirade would shock her back into fear-mode as she endured Elaine's physical abuse.

Later that same year, Elaine was pregnant again, this time with a girl. No one could believe that she had gotten pregnant in rapid succession with three children over four years. It seemed that Roger and Leann would have to adjust to a new reality that did not align with their understanding just a few years ago. Nothing seemed to make sense and no one knew any way to change it.

Leann now clearly understood that Elaine no longer considered her a member of the family. She had her two sons and a daughter on the way, her own children. Leann desperately missed her grandparents, who were not allowed to visit. Leann also longed for her father to be more present in her life. He was pulling farther and farther away from the family. Roger frequently worked longer hours or picked up extra work. Despite his years "clean" he was starting to drink more and more when he was actually home.

Because of his long absences, Elaine relied on Leann to help her with the two young boys, Caleb and Colin and, eventually, the new baby, Hannah. Leann was pulled out of school, or simply kept home, to babysit them while Elaine went to the doctor's office or out on errands. She was expected to contribute to the family, but was not included in family activities.

Trips to McDonald's meant Happy Meals for Elaine's children and a promise of a cheese sandwich for Leann once they got home. As a new rule, food was carefully locked away and only Elaine's children could have the treats that were bought at the grocery store. Leann watched as her siblings ate snack packs or fruit chews, but she was never allowed to have one herself. Roger had no idea that his daughter was being singled out; Elaine kept the inequality a secret from her husband.

One day Leann discovered a missing board at the base of the pantry that was only accessible from the basement steps. Leann would extend her arm through the hole and grab the closest treat she could find. She would then huddle against the wall lining the basement steps and quickly eat her stolen snack in silence, easing the hunger pains that always seemed to consume her.

****

"Snow day, Leann!" squealed Caleb.

Leann opened her eyes and looked out of her bedroom window. The whole sky was filled with fluffy snowflakes rapidly falling. She threw off her covers and went to the window. The hill and roads were covered in a smooth layer of white. Leann smiled at the clean, fresh view and patted Caleb on the head.

"Sledding?" he asked with smiling eyes.

"Sure, buddy."

Together they went down to breakfast and ate oatmeal before putting on snowsuits, gloves, and hats.

"I'm not going out there, Leann," Elaine announced. "You have to watch the kids if you wanna be outside today."

Leann scrunched her eyebrows. Only Elaine could ruin sledding on a snow day by making it sound like a chore.

"That's fine," she replied politely.

"Don't you sound all prissy," Elaine retorted. She then laughed at her comment as if it were a well-told joke. She continued saying "that's fine" over and over again in a high-pitched voice and laughing.

After eating, Leann herded the two small boys outside while baby Hannah napped. She got the sleds down from the garage hook, and positioned each boy safely in the sled together. They giggled and cheered the whole way down as Leann ran alongside the sled. After each run, Leann would pull the sled back up the hill while holding the boys' hands. Elaine was watching from the window and almost seemed happy; her smile was visible even through the frosted glass.

"Who wants hot cocoa?" she called, bringing out a tray of steaming mugs.

"Me!!!" the boys yelled.

They raced through the heavy snow to their mother and she handed each of them a mug.

"Here you go, Missy," she said, giving the last hot cocoa to Leann.

"Thanks," she replied as she lifted the steaming mug to her mouth.

The hot cocoa instantly burned her lips so she hesitated before drinking any more. Out of Elaine's sight, she put the mug on a snowy ledge to cool down.

Elaine was quietly chatting with the boys as they drank their warm treat. She glanced over at Leann and frowned.

"What's the problem with my hot cocoa, Leann? Not good enough for you?"

"No, it's just too hot," Leann muttered.

"Even when I try to be nice, you gotta get smart. Drink the damn cocoa like everybody else."

"Okay," Leann replied. She walked back over to her mug and laced her fingers around the handle. If the boys were drinking theirs, it must not be as hot as she thought it was. Without a second thought, Leann took a large gulp of the hot beverage and then her entire body seized.

The scalding liquid seared her tongue and throat as she swallowed. Her eyes widened, as she tasted blood and her tongue swelled in her mouth.

Her mouth began throbbing and tears filled her eyes. The cocoa was too hot for human consumption. Leann didn't know it then, but she had permanently damaged her mouth in her attempt to please her stepmother.

Chapter 7

"It is during our darkest moment that we must focus to see the light." -Aristotle

Grandma Eunice, Jack's first wife and Leann's maternal grandmother, was ill most of Leann's life. They very rarely got to see one another through the years, but Eunice worked hard to stay in Leann's life, even when Elaine made it difficult for outside family members to visit.

"Hey there, Elaine. It's me, Eunice," Leann heard her grandmother's voice projected from the answering machine. "Just wanted to see if you could use this bed we have for Leann." Her grandmother paused to take a labored breath. "We'll stop by later with it."

Even though the message sounded innocent, Leann knew that her grandmother was carefully crafting a way to get a bed into the house before Elaine could refuse it.

Later that day, a truck pulled up with a wrapped bed frame. Leann suppressed a smile as she peeked out the window. Fortunately her father was home from work, a fact that she was also sure her grandmother knew. Both her father and Elaine walked out to the truck to inspect the delivery.

When Leann saw them bringing it inside she felt anxious about her response; should she be grateful and polite, but not too excited? Should she hide altogether? She decided to stay out of sight until someone called for her. Eventually Elaine called her name and Leann quickly came to the door of her room.

Before her was a fully assembled cream-colored bed with flowers painted delicately along the headboard. There was no way she could hold back the grin and wide-eyed stare that took over her face.

"Oh my!" she whispered.

"Well, say thank you to your Grandma Eunice. You know we can't afford to get you something this fancy. Go on," Elaine insisted.

"Thank you sooooooo much, Grandma!" Leann sang as she embraced Eunice's hunched frame.

"Oh sweetheart, it was nothing. I just wanted to help out your daddy and Elaine." Eunice was still trying to make sure she didn't appear to be spoiling Leann.

"Well, we really appreciate it, Eunice. It's very sweet of you," Roger chimed in, placing a gentle hand on Eunice's back.

"Alright, I'm off. Don't want to interrupt your evening." Eunice smiled directly at Elaine. "You got permission from your folks to come over to my place tomorrow, Leann," she continued.

"Really? That's great!" Leann replied. She instantly regretted her enthusiastic response.

"Now, now, Leann, I need you for working. That's the deal. I have a terribly messy closet that needs organized and I can hardly lift a thing myself. Can you help me get it in tip-top shape?" Eunice continued.

"Of course!" Leann said nodding profusely. "I can do anything you need."

"Well, I'm gonna see how this all works out when I pick her up tomorrow," Elaine finally said. "I'm not sure Leann is gonna be much help."

"Oh, okay," Eunice said with a look of concern. "We'll see how it goes this time. I know you want her to be a helper, so I'll stay on top of her."

"Good, because if she's getting out of Saturday chores here, I definitely want her working if she's at your place."

"Sounds like a plan," Eunice said with a weak smile.

The next day Elaine dropped off Leann and invited herself in to see the focus of the day's cleaning mission. When it seemed she was satisfied with the amount of work Leann had before her, she decided to leave and run some errands until later that evening.

As soon as Elaine's car pulled out of Eunice's driveway, Eunice reached for Leann's hand.

"Come on, sweetheart."

"Okay, Grandma, I'm ready to work!"

"No, don't worry about that silly closet," Eunice chuckled.

"But if Elaine comes back…" Leann's voice drifted off as her body tensed.

"Now, Leann, I'm not worried about that crazy woman. You and I need to go eat a nice lunch together. Aunt Angie is coming over in a little bit to clean while you and I catch up." She gently tugged on Leann's hand. "Ready for a sandwich and some chips…ohh, and how about some soda, too?"

Leann stared at her grandmother with shock. Then she felt a weight lift from her. It was a heaviness that she didn't even realize was there. She smiled and squeezed her grandmother's hand.

"Grandma that sounds so good. I'm starving."

They continued down the hallway to the kitchen, hand in hand.

Leann soon found that Elaine was happy to have her out of

the house, if it was for a good reason. Leann's 4th grade teacher, Ms. Wicks, suspected that physical abuse was still happening at home, but none of the protective services agencies could find grounds to take action. Ms. Wicks' response was similar to Eunice's: she simply made up a reason to get Leann out of the house as much as possible.

"Leann, I talked to your mom and asked if I could tutor you after school so we can get your grades up."

Leann's face twisted with anxiety.

"My grades are low?"

"Of course not, dear. But we could still try to get them even higher, right?" Ms. Wicks said with a smile.

Leann was confused until she reported to Ms. Wicks' house, just down the street from where she lived, for their first tutoring session.

"Okay, Leann, our first lesson is…how to make cookies!"

Leann looked around the kitchen and saw bags of sugar and flour stacked next to cookie sheets and mixing bowls.

"Really?" Leann questioned as she slid off her book-bag.

"Yep, you earned it! Now let's make some cookies!"

They both washed their hands and reviewed the recipe before diving into to their first baking lesson.

Over the next few months Leann met with Ms. Wicks for further tutoring that taught her about laughter, joy, silliness, and tasty snacks. Those afternoons with Ms. Wicks would forever remain some of the shining moments in Leann's childhood.

As 4th grade came to a close and summer approached, Leann had learned how to lead several different lives. She was completely herself at school and loved working with others or independently on projects. At her grandmother's house she could smile and laugh and cuddle with Eunice while Eunice's hired help completed a task like cleaning the basement or raking leaves as had been promised to Elaine.

Leann's life shifted dramatically when she got home. She was keenly aware that she had to suppress all of herself when she was in Elaine's house. On most days, Leann stayed away from Elaine and tried not to expect much alone time with her father. Roger continued to grow colder and more distant during the hours when he was home from work. Even though Leann was young, it was clear to her that her father was just as miserable as she was. He rarely smiled, except during silly moments with Leann and the two boys or when he gave hugs and kisses to baby Hannah.

Leann's life had developed a new rhythm, but surprises still popped up from time to time. One morning as Leann sat on her carpet square at Sunday school, she awkwardly pulled on the frilly dress Elaine had forced her to wear. The dress didn't fit her quite right, but that wasn't why Leann felt uncomfortable. She couldn't help thinking about the stylish outfit her grandparents had bought her. It was a matching skirt and top ensemble that made her feel cool as soon as she saw it.

Elaine took that outfit back to the store where her grandparents had bought it and chose this hideous dress instead. Leann had no doubt that Elaine wanted her to look bad. That was also the reason why she was wearing the oversized glasses Elaine picked out for her. Leann told her how ugly they were and begged for smaller frames that actually fit her face, but Elaine ignored her and insisted that she wear the eyeglasses that looked big enough for an adult.

The week prior, Leann actually felt like an adult when she was baptized in front of the entire church. She had gone in front of the congregation and, while wearing a long church gown, had been submerged into a large pool of water by the pastor. When Leann rose up out of the holy water, she knew she would have a friend in Jesus, even when times at home were tough. She had received a candle that day to symbolize the light she had inside of her. Leann vowed to keep that light burning no matter what.

As Leann abused the dress a bit more and shoved the heavy glasses up her nose, she felt compelled to look at the small window in the Sunday school classroom door.

There she saw a smiling, familiar face looking directly at her. It was her mother.

When Leann locked eyes with her mother, who must have recently been released from prison, Cindy's grin widened and she cocked her head to one side. She seemed to be assessing Leann's outfit and new glasses. Leann lowered her eyes for a moment, feeling embarrassed, but quickly looked again at the window to make sure her mother was still there. For some reason she felt frozen to her carpet square. An image of Elaine came to mind and Leann suddenly worried that her mother might be discovered in the hallway. Cindy stood in the window another minute, watching Leann pretend to listen to the Bible story, and then she gave Leann a wink and an air kiss before disappearing.

Leann sighed and squeezed her hands together. Somehow

she felt happy knowing that her mother had found her and stolen those moments with her, even if it was just a series of glances through a classroom window.

A few weeks later she overheard her grandmother Eunice telling a friend how Cindy was only home for a few weeks before getting arrested for prostitution and returning to a life of incarceration.

Elaine made sure that Leann knew everyone had heard about her mother's return to jail.

On a summer morning shortly thereafter, she reminded Leann, "You're going to end up in jail like your mom. You're going to flip burgers. There ain't no other way for you; like mother like daughter."

She then grabbed a wooden spoon and blocked Leann's way in the kitchen.

"I'm gonna ask you a question, Leann. Do you have anything you want to confess?"

Leann's mind raced, she had no idea what she had done or why Elaine was suddenly so angry.

"Last chance, Leann," Elaine said, raising the spoon.

"I don't know what I did. Can you just tell me what *you* think I did?"

Leann backed away from her stepmother while also knowing there was no escape from the beating she was about to receive. She felt her muscles tense as she braced herself for the first smack.

The first contact always felt sharp and fresh. As her physical punishment continued, Leann would go numb to the sensation, but the first hit was felt completely.

"You think I'm an idiot? You don't think I can tell you stole all those snack packs. They aren't for you. I didn't buy those for you! They are for *my* children, not you."

Leann then cowered as the wooden spoon repeatedly made contact with her head, back, and arms. She stood, because attempting to run meant a worse beating. Instead she tried to ignore the rising burn that emanated from each welt.

"You are just like your mother, you're a piece of shit; I'm gonna show you what happens to little girls who steal. They get locked up."

Elaine dug her nails into Leann's arm as she dragged her to the basement door.

"Get down there, now, I want you on the very bottom step," she said in a low voice.

Leann actually turned to look at Elaine. This punishment was different and she couldn't quite understand what was happening.

"Now!" Elaine's voice suddenly became shrill.

"What, why?" Leann sputtered.

Without responding, Elaine gave her a shove and Leann was suddenly in complete darkness as the basement door shut behind her.

The lock on the door handle made a distinct click and Leann heard Elaine's footsteps as she walked away.

She stood for a moment in the darkness and wondered when Elaine would be back for her. While she wasn't afraid of the dark, she didn't want to stay down in the drafty basement either.

The steps were cold under her bare feet since every aspect of the basement was unfinished, including the raw wood staircase.

Leann shifted her weight and heard the wood creak beneath her. This entertained her for a few moments, but then she lost interest. She leaned her forehead against the paneled basement door and listened for sounds on the other side. Leann could faintly make out the sound of her younger siblings in their bedrooms. They were probably getting dressed for the day. She hoped Elaine would be back to open the door after everyone was done in his or her rooms.

She continued to strain to hear what was happening at the far end of the house. It sounded like they were putting on shoes and going outside. Leann's stomach tightened when she thought of them leaving her alone in the house, still locked in the basement.

Suddenly she heard Elaine's footsteps come toward the basement. Leann slid her hand down the rough dry wall as she took two steps down and away from the door. She silently tiptoed the rest of the way down to the bottom step.

The door swung open and Leann blinked at the wall of light that filled her eyes.

"Here's some bread and water. This is what they eat in jail. Might as well get used to it. I'll let you out to go to the bathroom when we get back."

Elaine waited a moment while Leann walked back up the stairs. She thrust a glass of water and two slices of bread into Leann's chest. Leann quickly grabbed them both and then watched in horror as Elaine closed the basement door again.

"Let's go, kids!" Elaine called once before closing the house door and walking to the car.

Leann was now locked behind two sets of doors underneath the house with no light except for the faint sunshine that outlined the door.

Her chest filled with air, she held it for a few moments, and then slowly exhaled. She was alone, her body still throbbed from the wooden spoon, but she somehow felt safe.

She noticed the weight of the plastic glass of water and the flimsy slices of bread in her hands. Slowly she sunk down to sit on the top step. She put the water next to her and lifted one slice of bread to her mouth. Slowly she nibbled on the bread and tried to focus on how it felt in her mouth. Despite her rumbling belly, Leann continued to chew slowly so that her food would last longer. She knew that Elaine would be true to her word: only one bathroom break. Since she didn't mention any additional food, Leann assumed her next meal would be dinner once her father came home.

Would he find out that Elaine locked her in the basement? Would he stand up to her and tell her that she could never, ever do that again? She wanted to believe that he would come to her rescue, but he had grown so distant lately that she wasn't sure what he'd do. She knew she couldn't tell him since that automatically meant worse punishment once her dad was out of the house again.

Leann took another slow, long breath and put her head down on her arms on the top step. She was so tired and sore that the hard steps seemed almost comfortable. She drifted off to sleep curled up in the darkness.

A few hours later she jerked awake when she heard the key in the house door as Elaine and the kids entered the house. She immediately walked down a few steps and waited.

The doorknob shook from the other side of the door and Leann winced again when the door above her swung open.

"Hurry up and use the bathroom if you need to."

Leann walked up the stairs and past her siblings playing in the living room. She was overwhelmed by all of the noise and light everywhere. Once she got to the bathroom she allowed herself to think about how long she had been waiting to go; it had been hours.

After she slowly washed her hands in cool water and dried them meticulously on the fluffy towel, Leann reached for the door with a small hope that Elaine had forgotten about her and her punishment. For one moment, she imagined herself going to the toy bin and playing with some of her favorite toys with her younger siblings while Elaine watched her soap operas.

That wish quickly dissolved when she opened the bathroom door completely and saw Elaine standing at the basement door. One hand was on the doorknob and the other held the phone against her ear. She glared at Leann as she continued her conversation.

Leann slowly walked back towards the basement door only glancing at Elaine once when she got to the door. Elaine nodded her head towards the basement to indicate that's where Leann should go.

Leann, still in her pajamas, walked down the steps to the

middle of the staircase. She didn't even look back because she heard the door close and lock. She sat down on the step and leaned against the wall. She waited.

At 3:00pm, Leann heard the phone ring as it always did at that time. Leann knew her father was calling to say he was heading home from work. She couldn't help but sit up where she had been leaning against a step the moment before. She could sense that something was about to happen, but she had no idea what it could be.

The door clicked and then opened and Elaine stood over her, looking down.

"Come on. Go upstairs and put on some clothes. You can read in your room until dinner."

Leann was relieved, but not entirely surprised. Elaine often showed some level of kindness, right before Roger returned. Leann didn't understand why, but she was sure it had something to do with not wanting him to find out how she treated his daughter.

Leann bounded up the stairs and got dressed. She then grabbed a pile of books and flopped on her bed. The bed felt like luxury after sitting on the hard, wooden steps for so many hours. Leann read three books to herself before she heard her father enter the house. She read three more before she was called down for dinner.

The meal that night was the same as every other family meal and Leann was grateful that things felt somewhat normal again. She ate all of her food and drank two cups of milk. Her father commented once on her large appetite, but before she could reply, Elaine said that Leann had been fussy and refused to eat earlier that day. She then shot a look at Leann as if to challenge her to respond. Leann sat in silence and continued chewing.

The next morning Leann woke to Elaine standing over her. "Get dressed. Now."

"Okay, are we going somewhere?"

"*You* are," Elaine cryptically responded.

"Oh." For a moment she hoped she was going to her grandparents' house for the day, or maybe to Ms. Wicks' house for summer tutoring.

She quickly got dressed and followed Elaine downstairs. Right away she could sense that her father had already gone to work. The younger children were still in their beds, but Leann could hear some of their early-morning murmurings.

"Get down in the basement. If I do one thing this summer, I'm gonna show you what happens to girls like you and your mom. You both are just trash; doing drugs, flipping burgers, or sitting in jail. You need to learn now, because you're gonna end up just like her." Elaine was standing over Leann, almost hissing with anger.

Leann was completely confused, but she knew that when Elaine was as angry as she was in that moment, she could easily slip into physical brutality at any moment. Leann hoped that if she didn't say anything and stood politely that maybe Elaine would realize she was punishing her for no reason.

Instead, Elaine smacked Leann on the side of the head.

"What are you, deaf? Get your ass down there!"

Leann stumbled forward and walked halfway down the staircase.

"No, all the way down. You have to go to the bottom step; that's where I want you to stay."

Leann continued walking deeper into the darkness. When she got to the bottom, concrete step, she stopped and looked up to the doorway, but Elaine had already closed the door.

At some point during the day she gave Leann her water and slices of bread.

Later she used the bathroom.

At 3:00pm the phone rang and Leann was sent to her room to read.

She came down from her room at dinner and ate with everyone like it was a regular day.

The next day Leann did the exact same thing. And the day after that, and the day after that. She realized after the first week of sitting on the basement steps from sunrise until mid-afternoon that this punishment was never going to end. She somehow knew that she was going to spend her summer days locked in the cold, dark basement waiting for her father's afternoon call.

And she was right.

Each morning Elaine would wake Leann as soon as Roger left the house. She would usher her down the steps and to the basement without discussion or eye contact. Leann had stopped trying to make sense of her punishment; all she knew was she was supposedly just like her mother and needed to get used to being locked up.

She let the basement door close behind her and then made

her way to the last step in the staircase. Slowly she sat down.

The wooden steps creaked beneath her as she shifted her small frame. She could feel the ridges of the planks through her thin summer clothes as she leaned forward to hug her legs. Her gaunt frame folded onto itself as she curled forward into a ball. There she sat alone in the dark.

There was nowhere to look; the basement was one, giant concrete room. No lights, no windows.

Suddenly the routine noises from the family upstairs quieted as a heavy door slammed closed. In that same moment, she turned hopefully to the door at the top of the stairs. The door that blocked her from daylight, from other humans, and from freedom was still solidly closed. It firmly stood over her, blocking out almost all light and connection.

Except for one small line of yellow. There was complete darkness except for the slight gap between the bottom of the door and the kitchen tile. In that space some late morning sunshine reflected off the ceramic floor and announced itself confidently even though it was such a narrow space. That light was so warm and gentle that she decided to unfold herself and for several minutes she actually considered moving out of the darkness. She even allowed herself to stretch and eventually turn towards the light that was offered at the top of the unfinished stairs.

And then it happened: she decided to risk leaving her assigned place to get closer to the light; to allow it to soothe her. She turned her back to the darkness and focused on what lay ahead.

Slowly she put one hand, then another, on the steps in

front of her. One step at a time, she crawled upwards. She knew which wooden planks creaked and avoided them carefully so she wouldn't make a sound.

A smile started to form on her face as she realized the light above had warmth as well. It beckoned her as she got closer and closer still. The light cheered her on lovingly until she finally rested her chin on the top step.

It was the most comfort she had felt all day. The slice of light offered itself without rules, threats, or consequence. She felt at peace knowing that she could still find unconditional goodness, even as lonely darkness surrounded her.

It has to get better, she thought to herself. "Just wait," a voice whispered in her mind. Leann smiled slightly. She could wait.

Chapter 8

"You gain strength, courage & confidence by every experience in which you really stop to look fear in the face. You are able to say to yourself, 'I have lived through this horror. I can take the next thing that comes along'. You must do the thing you think you cannot do." –Eleanor Roosevelt

The middle school years seemed to invite another level of misery for Leann. Academically and socially, Leann fit in with her peers and often excelled in the school setting. But home, Leann was often the target of Elaine's frustrations.

"Hurry up and get off to school, Leann!" Elaine would yell most mornings to get the house locked up so she could take her children to the private school they attended.

Her children would pile into the car in matching Annapolis Christian Academy uniforms while Leann would walk to the bus stop, where she would wait for her ride to the local public school she attended. She'd pull her coat tightly around her frilly skirt and bedazzled shirt. Leann's stomach clenched when she thought about her outfit. Her grandmother had given her a very stylish pair of jeans and a shirt in her favorite color the week before. Elaine immediately took the new clothes back the store and exchanged them for the ugliest outfit available for purchase: a big pale blue skirt and a neon shirt that had pink rhinestones all over it.

This wasn't the first time that Elaine had taken Leann's things and used them however she wanted. Earlier that year, she had taken all of Leann's birthday money and purchased school supplies with it. Leann was keenly aware that her siblings never had to use any gift money for their own school supplies. They seemed to live in a posh world while Leann looked on with desire from the outside; she knew what she was missing by comparison.

When she arrived at school she saw her friend, Tracy, who

gave her a pinched smile.

"New outfit?" she asked, with eyebrows raised.

"Ugh, don't talk to me about this hideous thing. I look so stupid."

"Well, I have an extra pair of jeans in my locker if you want them," Tracy offered.

"Seriously? Please don't mess with me right now. Do you really have jeans I could borrow? I'd only wear them until the end of the day." Leann's voice got higher as her excitement grew.

"Yes, best friend. I have jeans." Tracy reached in her locker and pulled out a slim cut pair of dark washed blue jeans and handed to them to Leann with a chuckle. "Here you go, enjoy my jeans!"

Leann tucked them under her arm and ran to the bathroom down the hall, completely ignoring her open locker and her best friend in her haste.

Moments later, Leann reappeared with the same rhinestone top, but without the embarrassing skirt.

"Oh. My. God. You saved my life, Tracy. I will love you forever, " Leann gushed.

"I know, I know. Now put your silly skirt away and let's get to class. The bell is about to ring."

The girls gathered their books and headed in separate directions for their homeroom class.

Before Leann left the school that day, she quickly changed into her skirt and returned the jeans to Tracy. Tracy folded them and put them back into her locker in case Leann needed them again. The girls walked to the main exit together, smiling.

This practice continued for weeks until Elaine made a random visit to the school and asked to see Leann while she was in the middle of class. When she saw what Leann was wearing, she promised a severe punishment when Leann got home. She returned to the office and asked that they open Leann's locker. There she found notes that Leann and Tracy had exchanged discussing boys, the clothes Tracy would bring for her, and the money her grandparents often dropped off for school lunches.

Leann could see that Elaine was suppressing all of her rage as she read through the notes, but she didn't think the assistant principal noticed at all. He stood next to them in the hallway as if this was a regular parent visit. Leann wondered if parents often made unannounced searches of their children's lockers. Was this normal?

Since it was only 10 o'clock in the morning, Leann was sent back to class after changing back into her clothes from home. Elaine took the lunch money Leann's grandparents had dropped off for her the day before. She made a big show of holding up Leann's slim cheese sandwich to the assistant principal to prove that Leann already had a packed lunch and was a liar for trying to get more money from relatives. Again, the administrator didn't seem fazed by the exchange and escorted Elaine back to the main office to sign-out once she was done with her investigation.

Leann felt tense and irritable the rest of the day. She knew that Elaine would not calm down or forget about the clothes or the lunch money. Leann was positive that Elaine would only wait until the front door was completely closed before she started beating her with a wooden spoon or a spatula or whatever was in arm's reach.

She was right.

There was no question, by 7th grade, that Leann was an outsider in her own home. Elaine would make a point of excluding her: special trips for the family often meant Leann wouldn't get to participate.

The family's first trip to Disney World was a grand affair that lasted several days. When everyone was settled in the condo one afternoon, Leann heard Elaine tell Roger how disobedient Leann had been that day. Somehow she convinced him to leave his daughter behind when they went to Universal Studios the next morning.

Every other day the family would wake up, get dressed for all-day festivities and leave the condo after breakfast. On the day Leann was most excited for, the day of Universal Studios, they closed the condo door and left her behind. She sat on the pullout couch, watched daytime TV shows, and read her book until they returned around 8pm. Leann was heartbroken that she had missed the park she had been looking forward to the most.

She could tell her father was uncomfortable with the growing animosity Elaine showed his daughter, but he also resisted fighting back. He would sigh and rub his face as Elaine would go on and on about the fictitious things she claimed Leann had done. Leann could see her father withdrawing further from his family. She noticed that he was taking his anxiety meds more frequently and in bigger doses. Because they rarely had a moment alone together, and because she wouldn't know what to say, Leann never asked him how he was doing.

Her grandparents and several other family members were more vocal and would chastise Roger whenever they had his ear for a moment. Even though those times were infrequent, Leann would learn how much they distrusted Elaine.

Most of her relatives had learned to give things to Leann in small doses and hide other gifts altogether. Grandma Eunice got smart and stopped sending money that invariably would be taken by Elaine. Instead, she and Leann would take outings and leave no trace of their adventures.

Despite her grim home life, Leann realized an extended network of family and friends were still rooting for her happiness.

During the summer after her 7th grade year, Elaine's brother Gilbert moved in with them temporarily. He slept on the couch at night and seemed to lurk around the house during the day. Leann avoided him at every turn; there was something angry and broken about him that made her nervous. When she actually found herself near him, he would always find a way to touch her: a brush against her hip, an "accidental" grab of her breast, or a lingering touch down her arm. Even the idea of Gilbert sent waves of nausea through Leann.

One night Leann was startled awake and began choking. It took her a few moments to realize that Gilbert was on top of her with his arm over her mouth. He hissed for her to stop making noise, but Leann was too confused to understand what was happening. She continued to gasp and squirm under his weight until he put a pillow completely over her face.

The pillow made it impossible for her to breath and something inside of her knew that she had to lay still and silent if she wanted to live.

As if in confirmation, she heard Gilbert's whisper in her ear, "If you make any noise, I'll kill you."

She arched her neck so that she could get a sliver of air as he continued to press the pillow against her. Leann could hear him fumbling with the things on her side table and then she felt his hand, now covered in lotion, slid under her pajamas. As he pushed his fingers between her thighs, Leann could feel his erect penis pressing against her back. He inserted his fingers inside of her, but then suddenly withdrew.

She felt his weight shift off of her and the pillow slide away from her face.

"I'll be right back, if you move, I'll fucking kill you."

Leann waited until she could hear his footsteps descending the staircase before pushing the pillow completely off of her face.

She had heard his threat, but Leann decided that she wasn't going to wait for him to return. Silently, she pulled back her sheet and tiptoed down the hall towards her brothers' room. Both of them were sleeping soundly, completely unaware of the drama that was unfolding around them.

Leann heard Gilbert coming back up the stairs and in an instant, slid under her youngest brother's bed. A moment later, after he had discovered she was missing from her room, Gilbert came in and looked around Caleb's dresser, in the closet, and around each bed. Leann felt her breath begin to burn her lungs, but she didn't dare exhale. He took one last look around the room from the doorway, but never bent down to look under the bed. If he had, he would've instantly seen Leann pressed against the far corner of the wall.

She heard him return to her room and then go into the upstairs bathroom. The house was silent except for his movements: rustling the shower curtain, looking behind doors, down the stairs and in the kitchen, opening the coat closet.

Leann realized that she was breathing again; short, brisk breaths that distracted her, at first, from her tears. She felt a strain in her neck and realized she was completely tense and stiff, frozen in an awkward pose on the hard floor with her head grazing the underside of Caleb's bedframe. She noticed her brothers' relaxed breathing and gentle mumbles as they slept above her. Without much thought, Leann relaxed her head and rested it on her arm. She fell asleep as the tears continued to wet her face.

The next morning, she was startled awake by Elaine's screams.

"What are you doing in here? Why are you under Caleb's bed? You are the worst, Leann! Who do you think you are coming in here?"

Leann was shocked that Elaine noticed her so easily and crawled out of her protective hiding place. Her brothers looked as disoriented as she felt and all three children looked blankly at Elaine as she continued to rant.

"What do you have to say for yourself, Leann?" she asked and then waited.

"I was hiding from Gilbert. He came into my room and stuck his fingers inside of me. He said if I made any noise, he would kill me. When he left for a minute, I ran in here so he wouldn't hurt me anymore."

Instead of outrage against her brother, which Leann had hoped for, Elaine's eyes got wide and she ran out of the room towards her own bedroom.

Leann could hear Elaine recounting the story to Roger and emphasizing what a liar Leann was. Before Leann could think to move from her brothers' room, Elaine was back and screaming again.

"Do you know what a liar you are?! This is insane! You could get my brother arrested because of your lies. Is that why you're doing this? You want an innocent man to go to jail?"

Leann had no words left. All the courage she had since escaping her own bed the night before was now evaporating in the presence of Elaine's furious accusations.

Her father appeared in the doorway.

"Elaine, calm down. Have you even considered your brother may have done something? What if she is telling the truth?"

"Come downstairs and say it to his face. You tell your lies to the person your accusing. Let's see if you can do that!" Ignoring Roger, Elaine grabbed Leann's arm and dragged her down the stairs.

It was a nightmare Leann could never have imagined: Elaine's fingers digging into Leann's arm as she pulled her 12-year-old body down the stairs towards the man who had violated her body, and then threatened to kill her just the night before.

Gilbert was stiffly sitting on the couch in the living room. It was obvious he had heard all of the commotion upstairs that had just happened. Some part of Leann wondered why he was even still in the house, but then she realized that, like Elaine, Gilbert would not back down in a conflict.

"Gilbert, Leann has something to say," Elaine released Leann's arm and pushed her towards him. "Go ahead, let him hear what you think happened."

In a voice so small Leann had trouble hearing herself, she said, "You came into my room last night and got in bed with me. You covered my face with a pillow so no one could hear me scream. Then you stuck your fingers in my private parts."

Gilbert exploded off the couch.

"Are you kidding me right now? Did you practice that? Do you always lie like this? I could go to jail if anyone heard you say that. Why would you want me to go to jail? This is crazy!"

He stayed standing by the couch, cemented in his position of outrage. Elaine stood nearby, shaking her head and glaring at Leann. Leann could not endure another moment and ran out of the living room and back upstairs.

"There she goes. Now you see what I have to deal with," Elaine remarked as Leann raced back to her room.

Alone in her room, she cried herself to sleep.

When she woke up she heard her father and Gilbert arguing downstairs.

"Now. You must get out of my house right now. I don't know what happened, but you can't stay here, Gilbert."

"Fine. I don't want to stay here. Everyone in this house is crazy."

Leann could hear him shoving things into a plastic bag and mumbling to himself.

"I'll drive you to the bus stop downtown and you're not to come back to my house again," Roger informed him.

Leann then heard the men walk out of the house, but she wouldn't let herself completely exhale until she heard the sound of her father's truck backing down the driveway.

She pulled the covers back over her head for a moment and felt her entire body release the tension that she had been feeling. Not much in her home life had improved, but she knew she was at least safe from Gilbert now.

Eventually she crawled out of bed and took a shower. As she was toweling off Leann could hear her father return and park his truck in the driveway. She also recognized the sounds of her three younger siblings: Colin, Caleb, and Hannah. They were playing while Elaine was on the phone with fellow choir members. All the sounds of the house were normal, not great, but normal. Soon there was silence as they left for church.

Later that afternoon after everyone had returned from church and Leann had taken a nap, she heard a banging at the front door. The whole household seemed to pause and go silent. The TV still played the playful jingle of a commercial, but Leann could sense that no one was actually watching the screen.

The pounding resumed. Three loud bangs again shook the thick wooden door.

"Who the hell is making all that noise?" Roger growled.

Leann heard her father stomp towards the door. Leann peered out of her bedroom door and walked silently to the top step where she could see the entrance and her father place his hand on the doorknob.

As soon as his left hand turned the lock, the door burst open and her grandfather, Jack, barreled into the foyer. Leann was shocked to see he had a firm, two-hand grip on a long hunting rifle.

"Where's that slime ball, Gilbert, hiding?"

Roger reflexively moved away from Jack with his palms upward.

"He's gone Jack; I took him to the bus stop. He's never coming back here."

"You took him to the bus stop?! You let him leave? How could you let anyone do that to your child and then let them go?"

Elaine suddenly appeared next to Roger.

"You better get off our property if you know what's good for you," she interrupted.

"You better shut your mouth, woman, if you know what's good for you," Jack replied.

"We already took care of the situation, so you can mind your own business," Elaine spat.

"My granddaughter is my business."

"Whatever, take your ass out of our house or I'm calling the cops," Elaine declared, holding up a cordless phone.

Jack's face grew red, but he seemed hesitant to engage in any more words with Elaine.

"You're crazy. You'd better hope I never find your piece-of-shit brother," Jack said with authority.

The kind, social grandfather Leann knew was nowhere to be seen in the irate man downstairs. He was completely transformed into a rage-filled protector. Leann didn't realize how loved she was until that moment. She finally had the adult response she knew she needed; someone was finally angry on *her* behalf. Leann smiled through silent tears when she realized how long she had waited for someone to stand up for her.

Someone believed her and was willing to fight back.

Leann later found out that her dad had called Angie for pills that morning to help with his stress. When they were on the phone, he told Angie about what Gilbert had done. Word quickly got back to Jack and he promptly loaded his rifle and headed over to Roger and Elaine's house. Gilbert, of course, was long gone by the time he arrived.

The next day at school, Leann told Tracy about all of the drama at home. That afternoon an official from Children's Protection Services came again to the house. They insisted on a full investigation with a medical work-up the next day. The results were inconclusive because several days had passed since the assault.

Again, Leann knew she had people who cared about her. Even though she and Tracy never discussed the investigation, Leann was sure that she had told her mother, who had then reported it to the police.

Even though Gilbert never confessed to what he had done to Leann, he was later found guilty of molesting and raping his own daughter. Before dying of cancer a decade later, Leann's brother confronted him in his hospital room and told him he hoped Gilbert burned in hell for what he had done to Leann.

Gilbert said nothing, but began sobbing as Colin left him alone in his hospital bed.

Chapter 9

"I forgive people, but that doesn't mean I accept their behavior or trust them. I forgive them for me, so I can let go and move on with my life."

M iddle school was a period of growing independence for Leann and she was eager to get out of the house as much as possible. She started babysitting a neighbor's children who the family knew from church. She also started spending time with friends after school and at sleepovers. Things were still tense at home, but Leann knew she had friendships that could sustain her through all of Elaine's tirades.

Saturday day afternoon, as she packed for a sleepover at her friend Samantha's house, Leann thought about Gilbert and spontaneously shook from head to toe. His roving hands and heavy body on top of her didn't seem real anymore. The whole incident felt like a nightmare: so vivid, but surreal at the same time. The boys she saw in school and at church, especially her boyfriend, Derek, were so cute and playful. It was hard to imagine any of them growing up into the type of man who could hurt her.

"Leann, you ready?" she heard her dad call from the kitchen.

"Coming!"

Leann bounded down the steps with her overnight bag slung over her shoulder. She couldn't help smiling to herself knowing that she was going to have fun with some of her closest friends. Nothing could ruin her mood. Not even Elaine glaring at her as she put an arm around her father as they walked out the door.

"Thanks for driving me, Dad. I'm so excited!"

Roger laughed, a rare occurrence anymore, "I can tell, honey."

He gave her a kiss on the cheek when they pulled up to

Samantha's house and then he slowly drove off once he saw she was safely inside.

The night was exactly what Leann had hoped for: lots of laughs with friends who liked her for who she was. She felt safe as they snacked on junk food and drank root beer until their bellies became bloated. Samantha's parents appeared occasionally to make sure they had everything they needed and to remind them that the neighbors could hear their squeals and laughter. The girls promised to keep it down, but promptly went back to story-telling that required loud outbursts of support at various intervals.

Leann noticed another man, older than Samantha's father, staring at the girls from the doorway. He would walk solemnly by and stare at Leann with a stern look that she didn't understand.

"Don't worry about my grandfather, Leann, he's a creeper sometimes," Samantha said with a wave of her hand.

"Why is he even here?" Leann questioned.

"Oh, he's staying with us. I dunno. Just ignore him."

Leann glanced back over to the space where he had been standing and felt goose bumps even though she wasn't cold. She wrinkled her nose and then turned back to her friends.

"Leann, what do you want to sing for our Karaoke concert?"

Leann smiled and thought of all the songs she could sing. She ran over to the pile of CDs on the floor and looked for the perfect one. When she found the NSync CD she squealed with delight and decided to sing, "Bye, Bye, Bye".

Later that night the girls piled all of the sleeping bags together to make one enormous bed on the floor. They talked and giggled until Samantha's mom came and shushed them at 1am. Eventually the conversation completely stopped and all of the girls were asleep.

In the middle of the night Leann woke up to Samantha's grandfather hovering over her. He stared at her with threatening eyes and he felt her body underneath the sleeping bags. His hands were slower than Gilbert's, but Leann felt the same panic wash over her again.

At first, she felt like her body was frozen and her throat constricted. She wanted to move, scream, do something, but she felt like a statue. The other girls were right there; she wasn't alone so she knew she had to do something to get him off of her.

Leann heard a noise rise up in her and she shifted dramatically towards another girl who mumbled to herself as she woke up. In a brief flashback, Leann heard Gilbert's voice threatening her life all over again. She thought that if she didn't acknowledge Samantha's grandfather that he may lose interest and leave her alone. She decided to pretend to be asleep and kept rolling towards the girl next to her. Then suddenly her wish became true: Samantha's grandfather was gone. Leann was shocked how he suddenly disappeared and looked around the room to make sure he wasn't just out of sight.

Unable to fall back asleep, Leann stayed close to her friend and waited until sunrise to call her father to pick her up. She was aware now that being away from home wasn't necessarily safer than being within Elaine's reach.

****

"Your stepmom is a crazy woman and we all know it," Jessie blurted out loud. "It's ridiculous that she treats you differently than her other children."

Leann smiled to herself, knowing that Jessie was about to go off on a tangent about Elaine. Her rants always made Leann feel like she had a champion in her corner. Jessie would say what Leann always wished she could say herself.

"I'm so sick of her being fake to everyone down at the church. It just makes me ill; all those lies! She always pretends like she's the perfect mom, calling you Missy as if you two were close as can be."

Jessie shook her head and looked for her cigarettes. "If you two were so close, I don't think you would've come to my house with a black eye the other day."

"I know. She is evil. Plain and simple," Leann agreed quietly.

"Leann, I don't know how you survive that woman. She *is* just evil, you're right."

Jessie looked at Leann's downcast eyes.

"Honey, I know that this is a hard time for you right now. I can't imagine how you must feel, but I know God has big plans for you. Your future is gonna be bright. So bright."

Leann knew she was not expected to respond. She simply enjoyed listening to Jessie and would occasionally nod in agreement. Leann was technically over at Jessie's house to babysit her two young children, but in the year and a half that Leann had been "working" for her, Jessie rarely left the house. She'd pay

Leann for her time and talked a good game to Elaine, but she was mostly creating a way for Leann to get out of her house for a few hours each afternoon.

"You know, Leann, if your dad let me, I could be your legal guardian and you could just stay here. You're like a daughter to me and I don't mind having you around one bit."

"Oh, my gosh, please do that, Miss Jessie!" Leann begged.

"It's up to your dad, I mentioned it to Elaine and she was ready to sign the papers on the spot."

"Sign the papers? Does she get to decide, too?" Leann asked with confusion.

"Oh yes, somehow she is one of your official guardians."

"Worst guardian ever," Leann mumbled to herself. She thought back to the argument they'd had the night before. Elaine was still buying horrible outfits and forcing Leann to wear them to school. Leann was trying to fit into high school, but it wasn't easy when you dressed in frilly or baby-ish outfits. She was never allowed to wear blue jeans even though her siblings each owned several nice pairs.

Last night Leann had stood up for herself when Elaine found a pair of jeans in her book bag. She refused to tell her who had lent her the pants and Elaine confiscated the evidence to show Roger. Somehow she thought that he'd be on her side since Leann was "such a liar and always disrespectful."

"Maybe my dad will agree to it just because he's sick of her, too," Leann mused.

She thought back to the argument again. Her father had hardly taken Elaine's side, instead he grabbed the jeans and handed them to Leann. It took all of Leann's self-control not to smirk at Elaine in that moment. She took the jeans and disappeared to her room. Elaine started screaming at Roger and didn't stop for, what seemed like, hours.

"So we're just waiting on my dad?" Leann asked, coming out of her reverie.

"Yep. I don't know that he'll do it though," Jessie said with a resigned smile. It seemed like she wanted to give Leann hope without getting her too excited.

"Hmmm. I'm not sure, either. I think he feels bad about not being there when I was a baby; I don't know that he'll let me go again."

"I know. I worry that he may be thinking that way, too. You know he loves you, right? He just made a terrible decision when he hooked up with Elaine. She brings out the worst in him."

"I'll say," Leann said with a snort.

When papers were drafted, Elaine signed immediately, but they sat unsigned by Roger for weeks. He eventually announced that he couldn't sign away his rights as Leann's guardian. Leann was disappointed, but not completely surprised. She knew that he wouldn't make the decision as lightly as Elaine, but she had hoped he would do what was best for his daughter. There was no question in Leann's mind that living with Elaine was not the best situation available to her.

Now the lines were clear to everyone: Elaine wanted no relationship with her step-daughter and the feelings were shared completely by Leann. In the weeks that followed, they contin-

ued to battle over clothes, chores, and everything else an independent teen would hope to do. Elaine went through Leann's
book-bag daily looking for any notes, extra clothes, or snacks
that someone may have shared.

When Leann returned to the house after school the next day,
she found her room full of her younger brother's belongings.
Elaine had suddenly decided that each of her children needed
their own room.

Leann's bedroom would now be in the basement. The same
basement she was locked in every day a few summers ago. She
would be down in the dark expanse with the washer and dryer
and unfinished cement walls. When Leann slowly walked down
the wooden steps, she stopped at the last step. She stood for a
moment on the one step she had to sit on for hours each day.
From that step she had to squint to see her bed, dresser, and
desk positioned randomly in the center of the massive basement.
Leann could make out some new flooring that turned out to be
indoor/outdoor carpeting. It looked cheap and abrasive so she
kept her shoes on as she walked to her bed.

As she tried to understand everything she was seeing, Leann
heard the door at the top of the steps slam shut and Elaine's receding footsteps.

****

Leann soon found discreet ways to feel powerful and loved
carrying them out right in front of Elaine. She decided to buy
some thong underwear with her babysitting money and hide
them in the ceiling tiles of the basement when she wasn't wearing them. Leann knew that Elaine would not approve of the sexy

panties, which made it all the more exciting. Each day she would stand on top of her bed and pull a pair out to wear for the day. No one really knew of her rebellion, beyond her most trusted girlfriends, and she felt invigorated by having some say in what she wore.

On Thanksgiving Day that year, Leann was shocked to see her dad and Elaine arguing in the dining room when she came up to help make mashed potatoes. She walked past them as she headed to the kitchen and heard Elaine mention her name with disdain.

They were both looking at the dining room table and Elaine kept saying that it was "disgusting" and "whorish". Leann could not understand what they were looking at and walked closer to them, with a half peeled potato still in her hand.

"Oh, here she is now; our pride and joy," Elaine exclaimed sarcastically.

At that same moment her father turned from the table and Leann could suddenly see all of her thongs laid out from one end of the table to the other. She could see that Elaine had cut each thong and spread them length-wise across the polished wood. Her face contorted as she looked at Elaine.

"Why would you...?" but she didn't finish.

Elaine started her noisy tirade again, this time seemingly for Leann's benefit. She declared her "dirty" and "a bad influence" in her Christian home. As she continued, Leann backed away from the table and went out the side door of the house.

She tried to hold in her tears as she walked up to Jessie's house. Leann was reminded again that there was nowhere to hide from Elaine; she was baffled how she had found the underwear in the ceiling tiles. As she walked, head down, to Jessie's house she realized how grateful she was that she at least had some place safe to regroup. Jessie would listen to her and grimace at the actions of Elaine. Leann would have a brief respite before she'd have to sit down to Thanksgiving dinner with Elaine and all of her visiting relatives.

Later that evening, Leann felt disappointed with herself as she sat crying again at the children's table. Even though she thought she was strong enough to endure a dinner full of her stepmother's antics, she felt overwhelmed listening to Elaine talk about her with her sisters and cousins. The women were whispering loudly about Leann and her hopeless future as they ate pumpkin pie. They all agreed that she would end up in jail for prostitution or worse; just like her mother.

Leann's father was watching the football game with the rest of men of the family so there was no one to defend Leann or temper Elaine's wrath. Instead, the women openly sentenced Leann to a life of bad choices and terrible consequences.

Leann sat in silence, stomach clenched, tears gliding down her cheeks. She didn't even bother to raise a hand to wipe them away. In that moment, Leann realized she would never be defined by Elaine. There was no reason to justify this new belief, but she could tell it was her destiny to outshine any future her stepmother could predict for her. She felt a power growing inside of her that did not make sense at this exact moment, but she knew her future was going to be fulfilling and good. Leann understood that she could prove Elaine wrong and become more successful than anyone ever expected. She didn't know how she would do it, but Leann knew her day was coming.

Chapter 10

"You are good enough, smart enough, beautiful enough, strong enough. Believe it and stop letting insecurity run your life."
-Thema Davis

Leann ran to the wooden armoire next to her bed and picked up a vibrating phone that her grandmother had given her. She knew who was calling.

"Hey, Leann. What are you doing?"

"Hey, Derek! I'm just finishing my homework. What are *you* doing?"

"Actually, I was thinking we could hang out tonight if you think you could sneak out of that basement palace of yours," Derek teased.

"Ha. Ha. Don't be jealous of my indoor/outdoor carpeting," Leann replied with a laugh.

"No chance of that happening!" he chuckled at the idea.

"So anyway, funny guy, I can finish my homework and then we can meet up somewhere. What did you have in mind?"

"I dunno, want to meet me at the corner by Jay's house?" Derek asked.

Leann thought about the corner of her block that was midway between her house and Derek's best friend's house. It was a perfect place to meet and walk around the neighboring block once everyone in her house was asleep. It was one of their favorite "dates" when he was spending the night at Jay's house.

"That works. 10pm sound good?" she offered.

"Yeah, that's perfect. See you then, pretty lady."

"Oh my gosh, you are so corny, Derek!"

Derek laughed as he said goodbye and hung up. Leann closed the cell phone she kept hidden in her armoire and looked down at her Geometry homework. She grinned to herself and got back to work.

Later that night, Leann quietly opened the basement cellar door and walked silently down the driveway until she reached the sidewalk. She then continued to the meeting spot where Derek was already waiting for her. For hours, they held hands as they strolled through the quiet neighborhood. The night sky was clear and Leann felt a sense of peace and rebellion as she looked at the stars above. The two teenagers talked and walked until they felt tired enough to kiss goodnight and sneak back home.

They knew the church retreat was coming up in a week so they didn't feel as anxious to meet-up again late at night. Once they were in the van headed to the retreat center, they'd have more than enough time to spend together. Those retreats were like extended dates with little parental oversight.

Leann was so grateful that Elaine never expressed an interest in chaperoning any of those church events. Instead she made sure Leann was at the church with time to spare before departure. It was no secret that she wanted to see Leann leaving, but Leann made sure *she* never acted too excited about the trips. She never wanted the retreats to be taken away as a punishment. So far, Elaine didn't appear to have any idea how much Leann loved the escape and chance to have a romantic weekend with her boyfriend.

High school should have been a time for more independence, but aside from the church retreats, Leann felt just as restricted as ever. She felt like any fun she could possibly have would be a result of sneaking off behind her parents' backs. Her dad seemed somewhat aware of her growing defiance, but as with most conflicts, he chose not to get involved.

Leann was pretty sure that he had seen the pillows under the bedspread forming a lumpy version of Leann's body. He occasionally came down to get his laundry at 4am before work and would have realized Leann was not actually in the basement or under the covers. He never asked her where she went, but for some reason Leann knew he probably liked Derek and didn't mind them spending time together.

Leann eventually lost her virginity to Derek, but didn't have anyone to discuss it with beyond her girlfriends. She and Derek had often talked about how they were going to end up getting married once they were older. Sleeping with Derek that first time felt like the natural next step in their relationship. Their playful wrestling session one night ended with kisses, talk of future family plans, and then a banana condom.

"Eww, that smells like rotten fruit," Leann giggled.

"Sorry, Jay gave me this for a special moment," Derek paused looking at Leann with love, "and I definitely think this moment is pretty special."

Later that year, in the middle of winter, Leann was in the basement on the phone with Derek when Elaine came to the door at the top of the stairway and started screaming. Leann quickly got off the phone, threw it inside a shoe in her closet, and braced herself.

"I said get up here. Now!" Elaine bellowed.

"Coming. What's wrong?" Leann replied as she closed her closet door and headed back across the basement. She walked briskly to show Elaine she was trying to be attentive.

"You know exactly what's wrong. You make me sick and I cannot take it anymore!"

Leann finally reached the top of the staircase and looked at Elaine, who was panting and completely red in the face. Leann had no idea what was going on.

"Get out. I can't even look at you anymore. I have never been so disrespected in my life!"

"What? What's happening? I don't even know what's going on right now!" Leann countered.

"GET OUT!" Elaine screamed.

"Get out of the house?" Leann looked out the window and saw snow falling in heavy clumps. "It's snowing. Where do you want me to go?"

"I don't give a shit. Get out!"

"I don't even have shoes; I can't go out there!" Leann looked down at her feet. She was wearing flip-flops, sweatpants, and a thin top.

Elaine grabbed Leann's arm and pulled her to the door.

"Now. I don't care if you freeze to death. Get out of my house!"

Leann, almost in a fog, stumbled along next to Elaine and, in an instant, found herself outside in the snow. She heard the door slam and lock before she realized what had happened.

Again she looked down at her feet and the thin rubber sandals she was wearing. The snow and freezing air cut through her lightweight outfit and she felt the burn of extreme cold. It was as if her body was confused and had mistaken the chill for warmth.

In the next moment, Leann felt a wave of shivers wash over

her body. The pain of the icy temperatures was rocking her to her core. She turned and looked back at the house, expecting to see Elaine ready to let her back in now that she had learned her lesson. Even though Leann had no idea what she had done to upset Elaine, she was sure she had served her punishment by now. The house was dark. It looked like her stepmother had purposefully turned off all of the lights after she had locked the door.

Leann's body began violently shivering and she realized snow was forming a layer of white on her shirt and hair. She thought about her Grandma Eunice and her husband and wondered where she could go to call them for help.

A moment later she considered going to Jessie's house, but worried that Elaine would look for her there. Leann decided to head towards the 7Eleven a few miles away and stop in at Jessie's house just to call her grandparents. She didn't want to have any more interaction with Elaine tonight, if possible. Once she had a plan in mind, Leann stepped off the door stoop and headed down the driveway.

Her flip-flops slid as she went down the sloping drive and she clenched her toes to keep her sandals on her feet. Her toes felt oddly warm and she realized that probably meant they'd be numb soon. She couldn't see her feet due to the falling white everywhere and the snow that was kicked up onto to her feet as she trudged along the un-shoveled sidewalks.

Her heart sunk when she saw all the lights off in Jessie's house and the driveway empty. She only paused for a moment before continuing on to the 7Eleven.

As she walked, Leann pulled her arms into her shirt and

wrapped them around her torso. Leann kept a fast pace as she walked and found the perfect angle to hold her head so that she could shield her eyes from the wet flakes that were floating all around, yet still see where she was walking.

As she slid step by step through the snowy neighborhoods, she thought about her situation. What did she do to make Elaine so angry? Did Elaine find a note in her book bag? Did she think the baseboards weren't clean enough? Could she have found a fruit snack wrapper from the locked pantry? Did she find out Tracy was still bringing her a change of clothes to school each day? What if Elaine found the hidden cell phone from her grandmother? Could she know about Derek?

All the possible crimes swirled around in Leann's head until she felt as emotionally fatigued, as she was physically exhausted. After 30 minutes of walking, Leann's entire body ached from shivering and cold. Finally, she spotted the 7Eleven and crossed the empty street. She waited until she was through the store's parking lot before she pulled her arms back through her sleeves. They were dramatically cooler and quite wet once they were exposed, but Leann forced herself to wear her shirt properly so she could pull the heavy store doors open.

Once inside the warm building, she asked to use the phone to call her grandmother. Thankfully, Eunice answered after the second ring. Leann's teeth were clattering together as she explained where she was and how Elaine had locked her out of the house.

"We are on our way, sweetheart. I'm sending Angie to get you. It's gonna be okay."

"Coming now, Leann," she heard her aunt shout as a door slammed on the other end of the phone.

"I'll make you some hot cocoa and I'll start the shower so the water will be warm for you, honey."

Leann smiled and visualized her grandmother pulling out a box of cocoa mix.

"That sounds...sounds...great. Thank you so much, Grandma," Leann replied, stuttering from cold.

"Okay, sweetheart, see you in a few minutes."

"Okay," Leann said as she handed the phone back to the employee.

Moments later, Leann saw her grandmother's car pull into the empty parking lot. It was covered in snow, but Leann could see that there were two women in the front seats of the car.

"Mom?" Leann wondered aloud. She hadn't seen her mother since she was released from jail earlier that year.

"Leann, oh my god. You are frozen. Oh, that bitch is gonna get what's coming to her. You could've died! Oh my God, your whole body is shaking!" Leann's mother slipped off her coat and wrapped it around her daughter like a blanket.

"Come on. Let's get you in the car. You know Angie drove me here, she loves you so much. She's in the car making it warm for you. Swear to God, she and I are both gonna go back to jail after we kill that crazy bitch Elaine."

Leann couldn't respond, she just shuffled in the direction of the snow-covered car with her mother's arms around her shoulders. She crawled in the back seat of the car next to a toddler that Leann realized was her half-sister. Despite her exhaustion,

Leann smiled at her mother's little girl.

"Hey there, Tori! You look way cuter in-person than the photos I've seen of you. So tan in the middle of the winter!"

"Oh yeah, you two are meeting for the first time, right? She's my little brown girl; her daddy is Hispanic," Cindy added from the front seat.

"Yeah, I heard Grandma talking about that. You know, it's so sad that I'm never allowed to see you guys. I hate that it's once every blue moon."

"I know, honey, we're working on that. Your dad and Elaine make things way more difficult than they need to be."

"Amen," Leann replied with a snort.

"We're here!" Angie announced as she swung her mother's car into the snowy driveway.

Leann could see her grandmother's face peering out into the night through the front window of the house, looking eager and worried at the same time. Leann's emotions were almost exactly the same as her grandmother's; she felt excited to be safe with her family, but worried that Elaine would show up at any moment and demand she return home. Her mind raced thinking about what Elaine would do once she returned to the house; to her room in the basement.

"Come on, honey, unbuckle Tori and bring her in."

Leann snapped out of her anxiety when she turned to the toddler waiting patiently next to her. Tori smiled as she looked at her big sister fumbling with the straps of the car seat.

"I gotcha, you little cutie!" Leann whispered with a grin. She scooped Tori up in a full-armed embrace and spread their

mother's coat around them until it was covering them both. Together, they shuffled through the snow and towards the open
door of the house.

"Oh, Leann! Honey, you look frozen."

"Actually, I'm much better now!" Leann reassured her
grandmother, "This little munchkin warmed me right up, didn't
you?" she said as she squeezed Tori in another hug.

"Aww, you two are so sweet. Come on in and have some
hot cocoa," Eunice cooed. "It's so fun having all the girls here
while my hubby is in North Carolina visiting his 90-year-old
mother."

Eunice guided Leann down the hall.

"Your mother and Angie are already in the kitchen putting
marshmallows on top. Sound good?"

"Oh, marshmallows! Yes please, right, Tori? We like marshmallows!" Leann slid off her mother's coat and the toddler's
jacket as the two of them walked back to the kitchen.

For a moment, Leann relaxed and felt safe. The house was
secure and warm and she allowed herself to think only of her
cuddly sister, the women who loved her, and marshmallows.

Later that night, as Leann prepared for bed, borrowing
clothes and a towel from her grandmother, she felt herself growing tense as she brushed her teeth. She thought about how much
fun she had had with her mom and then her mind flashed to
Elaine. She imagined her learning about where she had gone
and losing her temper all over again. Even though Leann was
bundled up under layers of her grandmother's clothes and thick
winter socks, she could feel herself start to shiver.

Suddenly her stomach spontaneously clenched. She felt her insides shift dramatically and she lunged for the toilet. In an instant she threw up all of the snacks and hot cocoa she had joyfully consumed that night. She emptied her body of all the loving foods she'd eaten; all the safety she had felt. Leann's body was shaking uncontrollably and she leaned against the wall. Her shivering was now accompanied by a cold sweat that seemed to prickle up all over her body. When she tried to take a deep breath, she felt her chest constrict and instead she could only inhale shallow, urgent gasps.

"Oh shit, Leann. Oh, man, you poor girl!" Angie said as she threw the bathroom door open.

Angie sat down next to Leann and started rubbing her back. Leann felt her gently pull the wet hair away from face.

"You are so upset, honey. I don't think you are sick, Leann, I think you're having an anxiety attack. You poor thing! I know your evil stepmom is the one stressing you out."

Leann began rocking back and forth when Angie mentioned Elaine. She knew the longer she was at her grandmother's house "having fun", the more punishment she'd receive once she returned home.

"You need to take some of these, Leann. Your body needs to calm down before you really do some damage."

Leann felt her breathing calm. Her first thought was that she wanted to convince Angie that she was fine. She wasn't quite sure why she thought that, until she saw Angie reach inside her pocket.

Angie offered a small, broken pill, "It's only a half…it will calm your nerves. You know your dad takes some of these to handle all the shit Elaine puts him through. Just take it, honey."

Now she knew why she subconsciously tried to calm herself down. She hated the drugs her father took on a regular basis. He probably didn't realize that she watched him pop the pills throughout the evening when he was home with his wife and children, but Leann was very aware of his dependence on the small bottles of pills he got from both his doctor and Angie.

Leann reluctantly took the pill from Angie and put it to her mouth. She opened her lips slightly and pretended to swallow it without water.

"Good girl, you'll be feeling better soon. You just need a good night's sleep."

"Thanks, Angie. Can I use the bathroom for a minute?"

"Of course! I'll go make sure your bed is ready," Angie said with a gentle grin as she backed out of the bathroom and closed the door.

As soon as Leann was alone she threw the pill in the toilet and let out a resigned breath. She had flashbacks to her mother hunched over the "sugar" on the table. Leann shook her head as she thought about how her mother must have started on her path to drug use. Leann swore she would never take any pills or drugs, no matter how innocent they seemed to be.

The next day, Leann's father came to get her. He greeted all the women, but their disapproval was palpable; he had failed to protect Leann yet again. Father and daughter walked through the settled snow to his truck and returned home without much conversation. Leann was relieved that Elaine and the children were not there when she arrived.

Over the next few days Elaine seemed to "punish" Leann by ignoring her completely. Leann could not have been more grateful.

****

By 10th grade some things had changed and some things had stayed the same: Leann tried out for JV cheerleading and was thrilled when she found out she made the team. She now had a structured activity that kept her away from home. Her grandmother would still drop off lunch money for her, but now she was careful to only bring money for that day. Elaine had recently found the stash of money Leann kept in her locker during another one of her random searches. Leann and her grandmother decided that they shouldn't risk getting caught again so they now met up for a money hand-off on a daily basis outside the main office.

Her grandmother, and all other family members, stopped buying Leann clothes. They finally understood that Elaine would promptly return whatever they gave Leann back to the store. Instead, they'd give Leann cash, which was only slightly better. Elaine would make Leann buy all of her own school supplies with her birthday money; whereas, her own children still had their supplies provided for them.

Eventually all of Leann's family members resorted to occasional outings with her to spoil her with "gifts" of experiences instead of tangible things that could be taken away.

Leann's father had not completely caught on to the new systems in place or the consistent way Elaine took Leann's presents. On Christmas morning, he seemed shocked when the children were going through their loaded stockings and Leann's was empty. Leann sat quietly with her stocking while her younger siblings opened gift after gift until her father noticed.

"Leann, why aren't you opening your stuff?"

"Dad, there's nothing in here."

"Are you kidding me?"

"No," she held up her limp stocking for him to see.

Roger stood up from the couch and marched to the kitchen where Elaine was fixing her coffee. Leann could hear raised whispers, "Why the hell isn't there…" "She's too old for gifts…" "You're the meanest woman…" "She doesn't deserve any…"

Leann's father and Elaine returned to the living room with forced grins, as if nothing had happened. Elaine immediately started taking photos of her children with all of their Christmas treats. Roger returned to his place on the couch.

"Hey, Leann. Can you run and get my iced tea? I think I left it on the counter in there."

"Sure, dad." Leann suspected her father was sending her on a fake errand, but she wasn't sure why.

When she returned with his tea, he insisted that she "check her stocking again in case something small was in there."

Leann looked at her father and tried not to smile. As she reached into her stocking again, she felt a crisp rectangle of paper.

"Dad!" Leann squealed as she pulled a one-hundred-dollar bill out of her previously empty stocking.

"Guess you didn't look hard enough last time," he said with

a shrug.

Leann didn't look over at Elaine, but she could feel her staring at the two of them. Leann knew she wouldn't coo over her gift like she would if it was one of her own children, but for some reason Leann was still shocked when Elaine took her money the very next day.

"I'm sick of your back talk, young lady" was her only explanation of the consequence.

Leann never bothered to tell her father; it simply wasn't worth it.

By the end of her 10th grade year, Leann felt less connected with her father and more alone than ever. She endured Elaine's accusatory rants about stealing, lying, and cheating on a daily basis.

"Leann, you are trash, just like your mother. I'm never surprised at what you do. If you don't end up in jail, the world just doesn't make sense."

When Leann did respond to Elaine's insults, the interaction would immediately escalate to a screaming battle between the two of them. Fortunately, Elaine was rarely physically abusive any more, instead she would torment Leann emotionally. Leann was as tall as her stepmother now, but thin and muscular. Elaine would threaten Leann with punishments like missing Homecoming or staying in the house all weekend.

"Leann, where the hell did this phone come from?" Elaine demanded one afternoon. She held Leann's formerly secret cell phone in her raised hand.

"I don't know."

"You are such a liar! I read all the texts. You and Derek, are always sending these sick messages back and forth. I can't wait to tell your father that you're a whore. You're gonna end up pregnant any day now…if you're not already!"

"Shut up, Elaine. You are the rudest woman on Earth."

"Don't you dare tell me to shut up, you brat! This is my house and you will show respect."

"What, like you show me? You are the most disrespectful witch I've ever met!"

Elaine responded by lifting the chair next to her and throwing it across the kitchen at Leann.

The chair landed against Leann's legs and she felt a wave of pain fire up her calf.

"Are you kidding me? Now you're throwing chairs?" Leann said with disgust.

Elaine said nothing and stood fuming in the same spot. Leann paused one second and picked up the chair and threw it right back at Elaine.

"I hate you and cannot live in this house anymore. You're evil!" Leann erupted.

As soon as the chair collided with Elaine, Leann turned and ran out of the house in her bare feet. She felt adrenaline surging through her veins as she took one powerful stride after another towards her grandmother's house. She knew she was starting something new and big, but it was also scary to think about Elaine ruining it all yet again.

As she ran, Leann decided not to give Elaine any more power in her life. She focused on her bare feet running strong and hard against the concrete sidewalk. Her breathing was deep as it filled her lungs. She could feel her arms swinging, bent at the elbow, by her sides. They were propelling her forward, towards her future.

Leann was on her way.

Chapter 11

"You fought battles, overcame obstacles. You had a goal, gave it your soul. You worked hard, went the extra yard. You gave it your all, you stand tall."

Leann was only slightly out of breath when she reached her friend's house in the neighborhood. She had run a half a mile in her bare feet. When her friend answered the door, Leann asked to borrow a pair of flip flops and used their phone to call Vicky. Leann's ally showed up a few minutes later in her yellow Mustang convertible. Once Leann was in the passenger seat, Vicky tore out of the neighborhood at a high speed, en route to Leann's grandmother Eunice's house.

The song "Young" was blaring on the radio and Vicky turned to Leann.

"So perfect! Hopefully this will cheer you up, girl. I'm so happy you're out of that house!"

"Me, too!" Leann said grinning from the passenger seat.

"Wanna take a quick trip to the beach before I drop you off at Granny's house?" Vicky asked sarcastically.

"You're crazy, I can't do that all the time," Leann responded.

"All the time?"

"Yes, I feel like Janie is always trying to get us to do bad stuff, like skip class or run off to the beach. You, Trish, Tracey, and Janie are always up for craziness."

"Don't act like you're some goody two shoes, you know you're always up for having a little fun in your drama-filled life."

"Yeah, a little, but Janie is always writing fake passes to get me out of class to cut school. I need to graduate; I don't know about the rest of you."

"Oh please. You know we're all gonna graduate. We all

have decent grades; we'll be fine. Besides, everyone skips school from time to time."

"I know; I just don't want to add any more fuel to Elaine right now. I'm hoping my grandparents take me in because I am so done with her at this point. I'm too old for the shit she puts me through."

At that moment Vicky pulled into their narrow driveway. Leann got out of the car after hugging Vicky and walked slowly up the concrete path of her grandparents' small, two-bedroom cottage. She paused only for a moment before knocking on the front door.

Her grandmother's husband, Tim, suddenly appeared before her with a surprised look that quickly turned to gentle smile.

"Hey there, Leann. You alright?"

"Yes. I'm fine, but I need to talk to you and my grandmother, if that's okay."

"Of course. I'll get her and grab you a cup of water. Come right in," he said as he stepped to the side while still holding the outward swinging door open with one long arm.

Leann sat on the soft sofa in the front living room and looked around. Everything was so familiar, but she was seeing it with new eyes. She realized how different this house felt from the one she had just left. When she was here, she always felt safe and relaxed; as if she exhaled completely when she passed through the front door.

"Leann! Are you okay, honey? You look all flushed!" Eunice observed as she shuffled in the room.

"I'm fine, but I can't go back to that house. Ever."

Leann's words hung in the air as both Eunice and Tim thought about the idea of their granddaughter being on her own. Of course she was too young; she'd have to stay somewhere with family, perhaps. It was impossible for Eunice to overlook the fact that she had already raised two daughters: Cindy and Angie, who had fallen into the grips of drugs and prostitution. Eunice and Tim were done raising their son, Timmy, and they were relieved and grateful that he was turning out to be a well-adjusted young man, considering all of the influences around him.

Looking at Leann on the couch, they knew they had to help her, too. The family would need to expand again to accommodate another member. Even though they knew they would take her in, they were momentarily overwhelmed at the thought of raising a teenager at their ages. It was temporary, they told themselves, Leann would graduate soon enough, but more importantly, it was the right thing to do.

With a look of understanding between Eunice and Tim, they welcomed Leann into their home for as long as she needed to stay. Tim helped her get settled while Eunice left the room to call Elaine and Roger.

Eunice knew how to handle Elaine at this point. While on the phone with her, Eunice conceded that Leann was a handful and convinced Elaine that it was easier to keep Leann at her house, and out of Elaine's way for the time being.

Not surprisingly, Elaine had her version of the final conflict; she said that Leann had attacked her and needed to live somewhere else for everyone's safety. It was decided she could stay with Eunice and Tim.

Later that year, Leann grew into her new freedom away from Elaine even further when she got her learner's permit to drive. Her friend Vicky took her to the MVA and they contacted her mother, Cindy for assistance. Leann would have preferred to ask her father to sign-off as her parent on all of the forms, but Elaine strictly forbade him from supporting Leann's efforts to get a driver's license.

Getting Leann's mother to help was a mammoth task in itself: Cindy was usually tied up in her work-release program and could not deviate from her required schedule. Somehow Cindy was able to convince her supervisor to let her leave her assignment a little early the day of Leann's driving test. Vicky and Leann scooped her up at the bus stop across the street from her job and drove her to the MVA. She appeared in the MVA briefly, just long enough to sign off as Leann's parent, and then she returned to the bus stop as if she had not deviated from her routine. Leann was thrilled to get her permit that day, but she didn't get her actual driver's license until graduating a year later.

Her remaining high school years were filled with highs and lows. After so many years of love and support, Leann and Derek broke up. It was the right decision, but the impact of that relationship would be felt in every other romantic relationship Leann had in the future.

Justin became Leann's new flame when she started her senior year of high school. He was the type of guy Leann could imagine marrying; in fact, she already adored his mother Marlena. Leann and Justin met at Mikie's and spent most of their final year in high school at work or on dates when they weren't in school.

One afternoon when it was particularly slow at the restaurant, Leann's shift was cut early. She planned to wait for her ride home with Marlena, but realized that Justin's mom wouldn't be able to pick her up until 9pm.

Justin offered to drive her home, but Leann hesitated because she wasn't allowed in cars with boys. She was forbidden from riding in cars with any teenagers, but boys in particular. Even though she wasn't living with Elaine anymore, Leann still followed some of her rules out of fear.

"No, I can't. I'll get in a ton of trouble if Elaine finds out. I just don't want to end up living with her again. Besides my grandparents are down in North Carolina, I don't want to get them in trouble, too. I'll figure something out," Leann reasoned.

"What are you going to figure out? My mom usually drives you home and she's not going to be able to get you for *hours*. Just come with me. We can have a little fun and then I'll bring you right back here. No one will even know you got out of work early."

Justin smiled and reached for Leann's hand.

"Arggh, why are you so cute? Fine."

Leann and Justin kissed for a moment to seal the deal and then they climbed into his black S10 truck.

Leann knew where they were headed before Justin even started driving. All of the teens in the area went to Ritchie Highway to drive their cars and look at other cars that were passing by. Justin grinned and waved to his friends as he steered the truck in a mall parking lot. They both got out at the same time and met their friends with hugs and high fives.

Leann's best friend, Vicky, squealed with delight when she saw them show up. She ran across the parking lot and hugged Leann.

"I can't believe you're here; I thought you were working!"

"I was, but it was dead so they let me go early."

"Awesome for me! It feels just like when we skip school, but this time we don't have to worry about being caught."

Another friend walked over from his yellow Cavalier and joined the three of them next to Justin's truck. Justin reached out and shook his best friend's hand.

"Hey, man, are we ever gonna finish that street race? You know I'm gonna beat you and your S10's ass. My car can outrun you any day," he said with a smirk.

"Ha," Justin laughed, "You're on, Dan. I'm not worried."

"You both better be prepared to lose," Vicky chimed in. "You know my Mustang will dominate in any race. You don't want to test me and my yellow Mustang!"

"Alright, everybody. Stop showing off, I feel like everyone is looking at us," Leann interrupted. "I just want to hang out and maybe get some ice cream later. No more car stuff."

"Okay, baby. We'll talk cars later. Let's go walk around." Justin put his arm around Leann and smiled at their friends, "Guys, I gotta go. I don't want to be on Leann's shit list today."

Leann chuckled, "You're a smart guy."

She grabbed his hand at her waist and they headed to the

closest entrance.

After an hour, Leann was ready for her secret rendezvous to end. Justin stopped by an ice cream shop in the mall and bought her a soft serve ice cream in a clear plastic bowl before they made their way back to his truck.

"Why didn't you get me a cone?" Leann asked when he handed it to her.

"I didn't want you to make a mess in my truck," Justin said, laughing.

"You're ridiculous, I'm a big girl. I know how to eat ice cream."

"I don't know about that…"

"What do you mean?" Leann pressed.

"Remember when you covered my car with confetti and wrote "marry me" on my window? Uggh, and those damn cans you tied to my bumper. I still get shit from people because you did that."

"That was so funny," Leann said, remembering the day she and Vicky had skipped school to mess with their boyfriends' cars at the neighboring high school.

"You were SO pissed!" Leann continued, laughing.

"I don't think it's that funny; it took me forever to clean up all that mess you made," Justin said frowning.

"Okay, babe. Sorry, but you brought it up. I'll eat my ice cream so carefully out of this freakin' cup. I promise not to mess up your precious truck ever again."

"Alright, alright…moving on. I'm gonna get you back to work so my mom can pick you up like nothing even happened."

"Thanks, babe," Leann grinned.

"...but first I gotta beat Dan's ass real quick," Justin added.

"Uggh, whatever. Just don't make me late getting back to work. I wanna be there before your mom pulls up."

"You are quite a wild woman," Justin teased.

"Whatever, if you knew my stepmom better, you'd know why it's not even worth it to break her rules. She's crazy and I am so glad I hardly have to deal with her anymore."

"I know, I was just giving you a hard time," Justin said reassuringly. He reached over and squeezed her thigh as they pulled up to a crowded intersection.

It took Leann a moment before she realized she recognized most of the drivers in the surrounding cars. Vicky revved her engine and winked over at Leann.

"I don't know, maybe we shouldn't do this, Justin." Leann thought aloud.

"What? A little car racing is exactly what you need right now. We're young, we need to be living wild and free!" Justin said with a wink. He revved his truck's engine and nodded to Vicky in the lane next to him.

"Whatever, Justin. I guess I'll just enjoy my ice cream while you all play around."

"I'm gonna beat 'em all, babe," he said in a whisper as the light turned green.

His truck tore through the intersection and down a long, straight stretch of highway. Leann started to smile in spite of her worries.

Vicky quickly took the lead with Dan close behind.

"Damn!" Justin cursed as he grinded his gears in an attempt to accelerate up the hill. He couldn't stand that he was staring at both Dan and Vicky's tail-lights.

"The light, Justin. Watch out!" Leann screamed over the engine as they reached the highest point in the incline.

"What?" he answered as he simultaneously saw the traffic signal ahead and both Vicky and Dan's cars slowing down.

The light was red and cars where already streaming through the intersection as Justin slammed on his brakes. His truck fish-tailed violently. He gripped the steering wheel, but Leann could tell he didn't have control of the vehicle. She clenched her ice cream bowl in one hand and grabbed the armrest with the other.

She could see that Dan's car had already crashed into Vicky's Mustang. It all appeared in slow motion as she saw her friends' cars pile up in front of her.

Justin's truck suddenly slammed into the back of Dan's Cavalier, which shoved the Cavalier up under Vicky's bumper. The crushing impact with Dan's car set off the two air bags in the truck and Justin and Leann were both thrown back against their headrests violently. The truck and the other cars erupted in a combination of noise and metal before they slid together to a final stop on the side of the road.

As the airbags deflated, Leann noticed a mix of burning and cold wetness. She felt the sharp pain of new, deep cuts on her face. When she slowly lifted her hand she also realized she was covered in melting ice cream mixed with warm blood.

Seemingly within moments, Leann could hear the distinct sirens of both an ambulance and a police car as they pulled up to the collision. In a daze, she was helped out of the mangled truck and led to the grassy median in the center of the highway. She was seated on the ground next to Vicky, who was teary-eyed and visibly shaking. Leann could tell she was crying because she was on the phone with her mom and probably worried about her Mustang. Gratefully, Leann couldn't see any injuries on her best friend.

"Hi there, I'm Robert," a voice interrupted.

Leann looked up as a man continued introducing himself.

"I'm a paramedic and I'm going to take care of you today. I need to contact your guardian first. Can you tell me who to call?"

Leann looked up at the urgent expression of the young EMT and she shook her head. He was moving so fast and Leann felt heavy and slow.

"Can I call your dad?"

Leann shook her head again; her father was hardly ever home now. He spent most of his time running the streets, and no one knew how to get in touch with him.

"Can I call your mom?"

Again slowly, Leann shook her head thinking about her mom in jail, but realized that Elaine might be her only option.

"My stepmom," she whispered.

"Great! I'll give her a quick call and then we'll patch you right up."

Leann closed her eyes as she waited. She thought briefly about Justin and wondered where he was.

"Yes, ma'am. I need you to authorize treatment so I can

dress your step-daughter's wounds." Leann heard Robert explain.

Leann heard his voice tighten as he politely argued the value of medical attention. She felt a pain rise up in her chest, not from the accident, but from the realization that Elaine would not give consent to her treatment.

"Ma'am?"

Leann looked up at Robert, the kind EMT who now looked perplexed.

"I am so sorry, but I could not get your stepmother to authorize treatment. Apparently, she's upset you were in a car with a boy and not at work. She was not very understanding," He said, shaking his head.

"You are pretty banged up, but not so bad that we take matters into our own hands. I'm really sorry that I can't help you more."

Leann closed her eyes. There was nothing to say. She wasn't necessarily surprised. She was, however, exhausted. Her entire body felt weak and lethargic at the same time.

Then she felt a gentle hand on her arm and heard Justin's mother's voice.

"Hey there, Leann."

Leann strained to open her eyes and she smiled at the sight of Marlena squatting next to her.

"You are a terrible mess, honey. I'm thanking Jesus that you and my stupid son are okay."

Leann smiled at that news.

"I was told that your awful stepmother won't come get you

or let any of these handsome paramedics help you, so I'm gonna just save the day instead."

Marlena chuckled to herself.

"Come on, sweet girl. Let's get you out of here." Marlena pulled Leann up off of the grass and put a loving arm around her.

Together they walked to where Justin was waiting for them in the family's Suburban. Tow trucks worked together to untangle the cars and Justin's truck in the background.

Marlena drove in silence back to her house. Once everyone was inside, she helped Leann get situated in a warm shower. She then used various items from her first aid kit to bandage Leann's cuts.

Leann wore Marlena's pajamas to bed that night, tucked-in lovingly in their spare bedroom. Leann slept soundly under the care of yet another mother figure.

Chapter 12

"There are so many people out there who will tell you that you can't. What you've got to do is turn around and say 'watch me'."

A little while later, Leann and Justin broke up after a silly fight. She felt adrift until Lisa, her coworker at Mikie's, assured her she'd rebound soon. Lisa decided to take Leann for a drive to the mall to get her mind off of the break-up.

On the way to the mall, a red Cavalier with a handsome driver pulled up beside them at a traffic light. The young man was thin with gelled blonde hair and light blue eyes that made Leann pause. He smiled at her playfully, and continued to drive slowly beside Lisa's car the entire way down Ritchie Highway.

Lisa couldn't stop laughing.

"This is so awesome. See guys already want you; forget about Justin. Someday he'll grow up and realize how good he had it with you," she reasoned as she lowered Leann's passenger window.

The driver and his passenger both smiled widely and whistled at the girls.

"What are you doing? We're going 15 mph! Oh my gosh, did you lock the window? I don't want to talk to these guys driving next to us! This is so embarrassing," Leann whined as she sunk down in her seat.

"Come on, this is the best revenge you could get! Let's pull over and talk to them."

"No," Leann shrieked.

Lisa ignored her and pulled into the mall parking lot, right where Leann and her ex-boyfriend had spent that fateful afternoon six months prior.

Lisa and the guys all jumped out of their cars and came

together in conversation. Leann's window was still locked while completely open, but she refused to get out of the car.

Lisa proceeded to tell the guys all about Leann's recent break-up, and how she was now a single lady looking for a nice guy.

"Well, before we hear your whole life story, maybe I should introduce myself," the driver said looking over to where Leann sat in the car.

The cute driver walked over to Leann's window and reached a hand inside.

"Hi, my name is James. I'm a nice guy, and I'm not really worried about dating right now. I just got out of a relationship myself and I could use a break from all that. Actually," he chuckled slightly, "it would be fun to hang out with cool people without any dating drama."

Leann looked up at James and his outstretched hand. She slowly lifted her hand to his, and felt his touch for the first time. His face looked friendly and gentle, and Leann instantly relaxed when she sensed he wouldn't rush her into another relationship.

"Cool, now we're friends. No big deal. Why don't you get out of this car and give your new friend a hug?" he said with another light-hearted chuckle.

"Fine," Leann responded, rolling her eyes.

She opened the door and met James in the parking lot for an easy hug. He was taller than she was and her face landed softly on his chest. She could smell his Curve cologne and smiled to herself. For a moment she forgot all about Justin.

Over the next few weeks, Leann and James texted back and

forth. Eventually they decided to plan an outing together. Leann worried that it might feel too much like a date, so she insisted that James bring a friend and she coerced Tracy to join them.

When the girls finally met up with James and his friend for the first time, Tracy was not impressed. Peter, her default companion on the double date, was a wild driver and seemed arrogant. Leann giggled at her friend's disgust, which lightened the mood. Over the course of the next few hours, the guys proved themselves to be gentlemen, even if they were rough around the edges. Even Tracy eventually relaxed and started enjoying herself.

Over the next few months, both of the guys grew on the girls and the foursome hung out on a regular basis. Soon, no one was worried about whether they were dating or not. In fact, their duel romance felt natural.

The guys were nearly perfect except for their immature tendency to sneak off with their ex-girlfriends when Leann and Tracy were unavailable. The best friends tried to convince themselves that the guys were faithful by cutting work to spy on them. They ultimately got fired from their jobs for obsessing over the guys as they tried to catch them in the act. Leann later got her job back after begging for forgiveness from her boss.

After a few weeks of worrying that James was still cheating on her, Leann decided to set him up on a three-way call with his ex-girlfriend. On the call, James agreed to have his "ex" come over to watch a movie and hook-up. Leann said nothing during the call, but later went to his house and saw them together. Her fears were confirmed. Leann refused to take his calls from that point on.

Tracy continued to date Peter and endured James' endless requests to help him get back together with Leann. Tracy refused to help him, in part, because she knew that Leann was better off with her former flame, Justin, whom she had just started dating again.

Justin and Leann were stronger than ever when they reunited. They felt lucky to have a second chance at love and celebrated every 12th grade milestone together. The grand finale, Senior Prom, that spring was magical and they seemed inseparable.

High school graduation day was a triumph for Leann. She walked across the stage with a smile filling her entire being. She waved to her grandparents who had purchased her cap and gown when Elaine refused to contribute any money from her father's household.

Leann tried not to think about the graduation announcements that her grandparents had also purchased. She knew it was a strain for them to pay $300 for the ornate cards, but they had all hoped that extended family members would celebrate her accomplishments and send money to help her start community college that fall.

Roger had even agreed to help raise money; he got the names and addresses of all of the family members Leann had come to know on Elaine's side. They were all eager to send money to help with college expenses until Elaine called each of them individually to tell them that Leann wasn't going to graduate, after all. It was a lie, of course, but none of her relatives thought to challenge her. They assumed Leann had, in fact, failed to make graduation requirements and would be in summer school to finish her credits. In the end, none of them acknowledged Leann's big day in any way.

Regardless, Leann had done it. She had graduated from high school and was looking forward to moving into an apartment of her own before starting her college courses.

One of the other milestones that Leann looked forward to that summer was reuniting with her grandfather Jack. His wife, Margo, didn't care for Eunice and the feeling was mutual. It had been years since Leann felt fully included in the holiday celebrations at her other grandparents' house, due to the rift between the two women. That was in addition to Elaine forbidding her to visit Jack and Margo during her younger years.

All of that was over now and Leann was counting down the days until she'd get to celebrate Thanksgiving with them in the fall.

Unfortunately, right after Leann moved into her apartment in August, she found out that her grandfather Jack had been diagnosed with pancreatic cancer. He lamented the fact that he would be cheated out of at least twenty years of life. Jack was realistic and he knew his diagnosis was dire; he wouldn't have much more time with his loved ones. The family gathered in grief and worry because Jack was the one who had always kept the family together.

He died in October.

There was never a chance to get together again for a cookout or holiday with Leann's beloved grandfather.

For most of Leann's life she was told that once she turned 18, she could spend time with her Jack again. She had repeated that promise to herself countless times through the years. She had waited until she was finally on her own to get truly excited about those special times spent in their loving home. Only when she was standing over her grandfather's casket did she completely understand how much she had lost.

The resentment towards Elaine began to consume Leann in that moment. All of those years, all of those memories, were gone now. Leann would never be able to connect with her grandfather again. It didn't matter that she waited until she was 18 and independent. It was too late and there wasn't anything anyone could do to right the wrong that was done to her.

****

Leann became driven to succeed and focused tirelessly on her college coursework and her three part-time jobs that she had to work to pay for classes. If she wasn't in class, Leann was waiting tables at Mikie's, riding the beer cart at the golf course, or working late nights at weddings held at Michael's 8th Ave.

Justin and Leann had recently broken up again because he felt pressured by his friends not to get so serious at such a young age. While this devastated Leann at first, she pushed through her hurt when Justin told her he had accidentally gotten a girl pregnant during a one-night stand. Leann decided that they could never be together again, even though she had thought he'd be her husband one day. Leann reasoned that it shouldn't hurt her as much as it did, but there was no way she would consider reconciling with Justin after this turn of events.

In another twist, Leann's father was in contact with Leann through all of her recent transitions. Roger and Leann had developed a strange support system for one another: he would call her from his new, undisclosed, location down south and cheer her on through each and every challenge she faced. Even though he couldn't stand to live with Elaine anymore, he was determined to be a more present father in Leann's life.

Leann was actually relieved he wasn't with Elaine anymore, but they both worried about the three children he left behind with her. Elaine complained to everyone about Roger's sudden abandonment. The church even donated money to the family on a regular basis to help ease her strain. All of that stopped when they learned that Roger had been sending money back home from his earnings off of illegal activities. Elaine stashed the cash in covert places throughout the house, but Leann's siblings found it when they went searching.

Leann still spent her free time with her best friends Vicky, Trish, and Tracey. Tracey was still dating Peter and they were now pregnant with their first baby. Leann was happy for the couple as they embraced family life. They bought a house on the Eastern Shore, and invited Leann to their first gathering that summer.

On her way to their new house, Leann pulled up to the toll booth behind a red Cavalier. When it was her turn to pay, the attendant informed her that the guy in the previous car had already paid her toll. Leann instantly realized that James was the driver and was surely bound for Tracy and Peter's house as well.

"Are you crazy Tracy, did you invite James to your house?" Leann screamed into her cell phone as she traversed the endless Bay Bridge.

"It's been years since you two saw each other, Leann. It'll be fine. He's single and mature. I think you two can act like grown adults tonight and help us celebrate our new house."

"Yeah, you're right. I can act like a perfect lady for your housewarming party. I'll be fine with a few drinks in me."

"That's right, we'll hook you up with some cocktails and it'll be no big deal."

When Leann arrived at the party she realized that she actually was looking forward to seeing James again. He seemed to feel the same way, and approached Leann as soon as she came in their friends' house.

"Hey! You're looking good, Leann."

"Thanks, you too," Leann said, feeling her face warm. "So, what girl got you all cleaned up for tonight?"

"No one, just me. I'm single now," James said with a smile.

"Ah. Good to know."

James offered to get Leann a cocktail and they caught up with each other over a few drinks. Later, the group divided up to play card games and stayed up drinking late into the night. Eventually players dropped out of the game and some even wandered off to sleep on couches around the house.

Long after midnight, Peter initiated a dare game for the visitors who were still awake. Leann didn't know how it got to the point that *she* had to accept a dare, but Peter challenged her to kiss James.

"No way," was Leann's instant reaction.

"You must; it's the game," Peter insisted curtly.

"Fine," Leann said. She leaned over and kissed James briefly on the lips.

Later, James received the same dare from Peter and did not hesitate to kiss Leann. Unlike their first "dare" kiss, this one lasted longer and sent shivers down Leann's whole body.

After the majority of the players grew tired, everyone searched for places to sleep. Tracy offered James and Leann the remaining single bed in their guest room. The two argued over who would get the bed, but ultimately decided to share it. Leann quickly grew nervous that James would attempt to rekindle their relationship further if they slept in such close proximity. She declared that they had to divide the small bed in half.

"No touching," she demanded.

"What do you think I can't be a gentleman? I have more respect for you than that," James said reassuringly.

"Okay," Leann said, looking him up and down. "You sleep against the wall."

James crawled across the bed and faced the wall and seemed to fall asleep instantly. Leann then crawled into the bed and stayed as close to the edge as she could. She decided that this night would be a test to see if they could respect one another's boundaries.

When she woke up the next morning, Leann was pleasantly surprised to see James in the exact same position next to her. His nose was still touching the wall and she could see he was curled up because she had pulled all the covers to her side of the bed.

She shouldn't have smiled, but she did. James looked so innocent as he shivered next to her. Leann instinctually grabbed a section of the bedspread and pulled it towards him. She gently covered him up and went back to sleep for a few more hours.

After a big breakfast, Leann prepared for her drive back home. James met her at her car as she stood by the driver's side door.

As they stood next to each other, Leann couldn't deny that she still had feelings for James. After a lingering hug goodbye, he gave her his new number with the instructions to call if she ever wanted to hang out again. He insisted that he had changed and matured since they had dated two years ago.

Leann didn't directly respond to his offer, but she took his information with a smile. She waited a week before she finally sent him a text. That was the moment they started to develop their relationship in earnest.

James became a loving presence in her life in the midst of so much transition and upheaval in college. They rekindled their romance slowly and built a friendship before seriously dating again.

After a slow start, Leann and James soon became inseparable. Before the end of her first year of college, Leann realized there was no reason why James shouldn't move in. She reasoned that they spent almost all of their free time together at her apartment. He agreed without hesitation and took on half of the household responsibilities from that point on.

That was the day they began their journey together as a committed team.

Chapter 13

"A beautiful life does not just happen, it is built daily by prayer, humility, sacrifice, and hard work."

After a year of "playing house" together, Leann and James daydreamed about a future that included children once Leann started her teaching career. They loved the idea of building a future together once they positioned themselves securely in the world.

Things shifted dramatically when Leann started to feel nauseous during her Psychology class one morning. During her break, she ran to the store for a pregnancy test. She wasn't truly worried about being pregnant because she was on birth control pills, but she wanted to rule out the possibility. What she didn't know at the time was that the antibiotics she'd been taking for an ear infection counteracted her birth control.

She took the First Response test in the bathroom stall on campus and was shocked when the result was positive. For a moment, she blacked out from panic. When Leann somewhat recovered, she called James and told him the news. She was bewildered when he announced that he was overjoyed at the prospect of being a father.

Leann, on the other hand, could not muster one positive thought about impending parenthood. All she could think about was the disappointment her family members would feel when they heard the news. She knew her grandma Eunice would be especially devastated after all of the hope she had invested in Leann.

While she worried about everyone's judgment, James proudly told every member of his family that he would soon become a father. He continued to be positive and encouraging as Leann tried to process how a new baby would impact her schooling.

"Just try to stay focused on the bright side, Leann. You have me. I'll be there helping out so you can finish school and become a teacher, just like you always wanted. We will just be a family, just a little sooner than we expected," James insisted.

Word spread quickly to all of Leann's friends and family. The response was mixed: Leann's friends were excited, but most of her family members were worried or even outraged. They predicted she would not be able to finish school while juggling motherhood.

Elaine announced to anyone who would listen that she had predicted this outcome and that Leann was "a piece of shit that would never amount to anything."

Other people's perceptions were the least of Leann's worries. She endured extreme morning sickness for the duration of her pregnancy. Fortunately, both James and her father were always supportive. Her grandmother Eunice, on the other hand, was inconsolable for most of the nine months.

"I feel like you made a fool of me, Leann. I believed in you and now you've gone and thrown your life away. I doubt you can finish school now," Eunice reasoned.

"That's not true! I'm going to finish college. I'm transferring to a university and it's all going to work out. I promise, grandma!" Leann declared.

She said it with passion and purpose, but Leann had no way of knowing how difficult it would be to keep that particular promise. Her morning sickness never passed after the first trimester as Tracy had predicted. Instead, Leann's illness grew worse until she was hospitalized for dehydration and weight loss. She couldn't eat or drink without a violent physical reaction from her body. She ended up losing ten pounds during her pregnancy.

Leann ended up finishing her spring semester in a hospital bed. She took her final exams electronically before undergoing a C-section. The baby had remained in a breeched position despite her doctor's repeated efforts to turn her.

"Oh my gosh, she's gorgeous," James announced when the doctor pulled their blood-covered daughter from Leann's abdomen.

It took all of Leann's willpower not to cry; she couldn't accept that she had become a mother. The first time she held her daughter, Madison, she went from peaceful to screaming in an instant.

"Here, take her back. She doesn't like me," Leann said tearfully to James as she handed the swaddled baby back to him.

The mother and daughter spent a full week in the hospital recovering, Leann from her C-section and Maddie from jaundice. During her stay alone in the room while her daughter received treatments, Leann felt like she was on an emotional rollercoaster. No one had told her about the hormonal crash that occurs right after a woman gives birth. She struggled with alternating sadness and feelings of hopelessness. After a week of torment, Leann felt her mindset stabilize and she was ready to step into her role of motherhood.

The family was finally complete and back home by May. It was the end of Leann's second year in college. They rested and grew comfortable in their togetherness.

A few months after they became parents, James proposed to Leann while they went jet skiing together. He had the ring tied to a small buoy with a note that said, "Will you marry me?"

Even though Leann said yes to the proposal, she knew that she wanted a long engagement until she finished her degree. She was transferring to Towson University the following month and she wanted her focus to be completely on school and her new family.

During those next few months, it took everything she had to earn enough money to pay her portion of the bills and to stay afloat in her college classes. Unfortunately, that didn't last long. Leann found herself bouncing checks because of her account's negative balance at the bank. She considered going on public assistance, but told herself if she did, she would get off of it as soon as possible. The final indication that they needed help was the day Leann went to a food bank after discovering there wasn't any food in the fridge and they had no money for groceries.

Halfway through the fall semester, Leann and James decided they had no choice but to apply for WICS assistance in order to provide for their growing family. Leann also convinced Towson University to recognize her independent status in order to qualify for financial aid. Both of her parents were again wrapped up in illegal activity, or in jail and were not able to contribute anything towards Leann's education.

Late nights of waiting tables and teething baby cries made studying a never-ending challenge that Leann wondered if she could endure. She knew that she didn't want to stay on public assistance, so she kept her focus on graduation and the promise of a steady paying job as a teacher.

In the meanwhile, Leann decided to try working as a consultant with a company that has now merged with Pure Romance™. Leann knew she could only work a few hours a week, but make at least triple what she had earned waiting tables in the same amount of time. Despite the easy money, she always told herself it was temporary. She spent hours working at her unpaid teaching internship, but she knew it would lead to a good salary as a teacher. She continually told herself that a career as a teacher would compensate her enough to quit all her other jobs.

Leann continued to juggle all of her roles as a mother, consultant, and student. The lowest point of her college experience came the night she was finalizing her student teaching portfolio with her baby girl crying in her arms.

"I know, honey. This stinks. I know. Mommy has to present this tomorrow so I can't stop and rock you right now. I know..." Leann tried in vain to comfort her daughter while James slept before his next shift began.

Suddenly the front door of the small, cottage-style home they were renting erupted in thunderous banging.

Leann ran to the peephole with the baby still in her arms and looked out into darkness.

"What going on? Who's there?" Leann asked through the thick wood.

"Leann! It's me! I need some money, honey," Leann's mother yelled.

"Mom? Oh my gosh. I can tell you're high. Get out of here

before the neighbors call the police!" Leann whispered through the door crack while bouncing the baby on her hip frantically.

"I just need some money, Leann. Open up!"

"NO, Mom. I don't have any money for us, let alone you and your drugs. Go now!" Leann pleaded.

Cindy banged some more as if she forgot that Leann was still standing on the other side of the door.

"Go, Mom!" Leann hissed again, hoping not to wake James. She worried about his ability to sleep since he seemed to work Toyota and AutoZone around the clock.

The banging ceased and Leann started to walk back to her project that was spread out across the kitchen table.

As soon as she sat down, there was an explosion of glass. Behind Leann, a large brick hurled through the glass bay window of the living room. Leann gasped as the glass flew across the couch and embedded itself into the carpeted floor.

Leann could see the muddy brick from the front garden that had done the damage; it sat heavy in the white carpet at her feet.

"Leann! It's me." Cindy announced herself from the demolished front window. She immediately started climbing through the jagged glass towards Leann.

Before Leann could respond, James was running into the room. He quickly scanned the space, the shattered glass, and the intruder.

"What the hell?" he looked about with wide eyes and an open mouth.

"James, take Maddie. I gotta go call the police. Don't tell my mom where I am. Here, take her." Leann shoved the toddler in his arms and ran in her bare feet to her car with her cell phone in hand. She silently crawled into the driver's seat and dialed 911.

Back inside the house, Cindy continued to make her way through the broken glass, slicing her skin open at every point of contact. Blood was now coming out of several wounds on Cindy's body, but she didn't seem to notice.

James stood in stunned silence as he watched, his arms still full of his squirming daughter.

Cindy finally looked up at him across the room.

"Well... aren't you gonna help me in?"

Within the hour, police officers took Cindy into custody and Leann was left with a blood-covered living room. The next morning, Leann boarded up the front window with cardboard and called a cleaner to treat the extensive dried blood on the brown couch and white carpet. She made the painful choice to take money set aside for the heating and electric to pay for the glass replacement and cleaning service. She then raced to class and presented her portfolio to her supervisors. Leann passed her review, the final requirement of her education program, and looked forward to graduation with relief.

When college graduation day finally arrived, it was bittersweet. Leann's dad had just been locked up on a possession charge and was at a correctional facility in Towson. Because he was being held near the college campus, Leann was able to stop by en route to the ceremony to see her dad while wearing her cap and gown.

"Hmmm. No hats normally... aw, go ahead." The guards said with a nod while looking through the security glass at Leann.

Roger's whole face lit up when he saw Leann through the glass of the visitor's booth. He smiled with tears filling his eyes and picked up the black phone cradled next to his head.

He whispered into the receiver as he wiped his cheeks, "Leann, I'm so sorry for everything. You did it; I knew you could do it."

Even though they couldn't hug, Leann felt his love envelop her.

"I know I wasn't there for you when you needed me the most. It doesn't mean I didn't love you," he paused. "I didn't realize how bad it was. I promise to be a better father once I get out of here in a few weeks."

"I know, Dad."

"I'm going to get my act together. I just need some time to get on my feet again. Now that Elaine filed for divorce and took everything, I'm not sure what I'll do, but I'll figure it out."

"Dad, I hope you know that you can always stay with us. I want you to be a part of my life and make up for lost time."

Later in the stadium, some of Leann's family members were in the bleachers cheering her on as she accepted her college diploma after earning a GPA of 3.85. She finally earned a Bachelor's of Science in Elementary Education. James and their daughter sat next to Leann's mother and aunt, both of whom arrived to the festivities high on pills. Eunice and her family were also there. Eunice looked prouder than ever as she watched her granddaughter keep her promise to finish college. She was there, despite her failing health, to show Leann that she was loved through all the hardships.

Elaine was the only family member who wasn't invited to the ceremony that day. In a final attempt to prove her worthiness, Leann had decided to send a graduation announcement to her stepmother. Leann wanted to show Elaine that she had done everything that she had told her she couldn't do. Elaine had predicted that Leann would never be anything more than a "hamburger flipper" and now she had completed her degree, despite all of the challenges she faced.

The announcement had included information about the reception, but Leann was still surprised to see Elaine walk through the door during her post-graduation festivities. Elaine mingled with the crowd, had a margarita, and told everyone how her influence had led to this monumental moment. She never spoke directly to Leann that day and left, without leaving a gift or even a card.

Chapter 14

"The world is the great
gymnasium where we
come to make ourselves strong."
Swami Vivekananda

Leann soon got a job offer from Anne Arundel County Public School (AACPS) district for a fourth grade teaching position at Marley Elementary School. The school served a low-income population that presented Leann with just the right amount of challenge she craved as a new teacher.

She was also acutely aware that she'd get to help fourth grade students just as Ms. Wicks had helped her so many years before. Her favorite teacher had changed the trajectory of her life, and now she had the potential to impact the many young lives she'd meet that year and in the years to follow.

At this time, Leann officially enrolled in the health insurance and teacher benefits offered by AACPS. She never submitted paperwork for public assistance from that point on. Leann again, had kept a promise that she had made to herself: never stay on food stamps or state-funded insurance longer than necessary.

Before the first day of school, Leann was finishing some last minute preparation in her classroom when she was called to the principal's office. She nervously walked to the front of the building and was disoriented when she saw Elaine standing in the office, holding a muffin.

"Oh Leann, I'm so happy for you," Elaine said, tears filling her eyes.

"Why are you here?" Leann wondered aloud.

"Don't you remember I used to bring you a muffin on your first day of school when you were little?"

Leann shook her head, vaguely remembering the two times

Elaine brought her a muffin at beginning of kindergarten and first-grade. Both times were before she had children of her own and became abusive towards Leann.

She took the muffin with a quiet "thank you," and turned to walk back to her classroom without another word. As Leann got farther and farther away from the woman who had made her childhood so difficult, so fraught with negativity and fear, she suddenly felt strong. She was stronger not because of Elaine's support as a mother figure, but just the opposite. Leann was strong because of the challenges throughout her life that she had faced and had overcome. Time and again, Leann had been tested. Now she realized that she had passed each and every test. Now she was sure that could be successful in all aspects of her life.

****

Leann didn't see Elaine again until the day she and James helped her father move his remaining possessions out of his former home. Roger quickly jumped out of the car as soon as their car came to a stop. He hustled past Elaine, who was standing on the side porch, arms crossed.

"So this is your mini-me? I heard she looked just like you. Don't want to bring her around me, I might beat her the same way I beat you," Elaine said, laughing as if she had told a clever joke.

"Did she just say that?" James muttered to Leann.

"Let's go," Leann said in response. "Dad, you got everything?"

Her father looked from Leann to Elaine as he descended the driveway.

Roger replied with a firm, "Yep!"

"Aww, so cute. Daddy has to move back in with his daughter. At least you found someone to take you in, Roger. I can't believe you'd let a druggie with a criminal record live with you and that baby, Missy."

In a silent pact, all the adults seemed to understand that the best response to Elaine was to ignore her. They all knew that Roger had been clean for years and had no intention of ruining the life he had rebuilt with his daughter. They all piled back in the car almost as quickly as they had gotten out.

As they reversed out of the driveway for the last time, Leann again realized her strength. She didn't need to fight back; all she had to do was keep moving forward. She was starting a new phase of her life with her fiancé, her father, and her daughter; people who inspired and supported her as she continued to grow.

****

By the end of Leann's first year of teaching she felt she was barely keeping her head above water with motherhood, career, and rebuilding her relationship with her father. In March she started to feel guilty for neglecting her grandma Eunice, who seemed to call at the most inconvenient times. Leann vowed to add her grandmother to her priority list.

During her planning period the next day, Leann finally sat down to call her grandmother so they could catch up before her students returned to class.

"Hello?" Tim answered.

"Hi, Tim! Can I talk to Grandma real quick?" Leann asked cheerfully.

"I wish you could," he replied slowly.

"Why? Is she sleeping?" Leann asked.

"No, she passed away last night. I found her cold as ice."

"Are you kidding me?" Leann said, anger filling her body. She could hear her grandmother's voice in her mind; Eunice had left several recorded messages on Leann's phone just that week. Leann felt sick thinking about all of missed opportunities to connect with her beloved grandmother that year. She knew Eunice had become increasing ill over the last few months in particular. Her death was not a surprise, but Leann still had trouble processing her absence.

Part of the reason she struggled was because Tim held a small memorial service for his late wife in North Carolina, but didn't invite any of her family members. Leann decided to hold her own ceremony one evening when she was in the house alone: she lit a single candle, thought of all the blessings she'd experienced because of Eunice, said goodbye, and cried until she had no more tears. Leann had a shift from grief to peace as she realized that she had made her grandmother proud. Leann made another promise to her grandmother in that moment; she would always strive for excellence so that she would continue to make her grandmother proud up in heaven.

****

Leann decided to go back to graduate school after her first year of teaching to build her overall knowledge and improve her classroom instruction. She continued teaching during the day yet found a way to balance her family, her studies, and her work as a consultant at Pure Romance™. Leann had realized over the years that she could make a good income as a consultant, and had even saved up enough to buy a house for her and her family. Teaching was not as lucrative as she had thought it would be, but she loved making a lasting impact with her students.

James continued to ask Leann to marry him; he was ready to set a date. He reminded her that they had hit all of their goals and milestones. James admitted that they were doing some things backwards, like starting a family before they were married, but he was determined to make their life together official.

Leann, on the other hand, was more hesitant over time because she knew that James, while a loving father, was an erratic partner. There were times when his moods were euphoric, but then he would plummet into states of uncontrollable anger. He never was physically dangerous, but the emotional toll wore on Leann through the years. She loved him, but was perplexed when she thought what it would mean to make the final commitment to be his wife.

Her concession to James was to work it out with couples' counselor. Soon they started attending weekly sessions together. The counselor identified James' erratic behavior as a key characteristic of a bipolar disorder. The counselor determined that James was an ideal candidate for medication, and Leann agreed to move forward with wedding plans, if James agreed to follow a treatment plan consistently.

After James was on medication for six months, Leann was emotionally ready to marry him without concern. His moods had improved dramatically, and he was the stable partner Leann had always needed.

Their wedding reception, which preceded the actual wedding date, was held in Marlena's backyard. Marlena had remained a strong mother figure in Leann's life through the years.

Everything on their big day was perfect: the DJ, the dance floor, the extensive lunch buffet, the stocked bar, and the dessert table. Everyone there had fun, but jokingly acknowledged how unusual the couple had been in their family development.

"Hey, Leann, how backwards can two people get? First you have a kid, then you have a party, and *then* you finally have a wedding. Oh and your reception is in the backyard of your ex-boyfriend's parents' house," Roger observed, laughing. "You are definitely my daughter; we're all a little dysfunctional. But if it works for you, it works for me!"

Leann laughed, "I know, I know. You're right, we are a crazy family. You gotta love Marlena though, she cares about James just like he's another son. That's why I always call her Mom 2."

Marlena heard her name and joined the conversation while smiling broadly.

"Can a girl get a hug from the bride-to-be?" Marlena teased.

"Of course! And I am so glad you're able to come to Turks and Caicos for our destination wedding. It will mean so much to have you there," Leann gushed.

"I would never miss it, my adopted daughter," Marlena said squeezing Leann's shoulders in a side hug.

"No way, she actually came," Roger interrupted, looking at someone behind Leann and Marlena. "I was sure she'd just drop your siblings off and leave. That lady always has to be the center of attention."

"What?" Leann asked while turning around.

Leann saw Elaine crossing the lawn and immediately de-cided to remain positive, no matter what happened next.

"It's fine, Dad. Nothing is going to steal my sunshine on my special day."

At that same moment, Vicky stumbled into Elaine's path. Leann could see that Vicky had been drinking and was in shock seeing Leann's stepmother at the reception. Vicky stood bolt up-right and started shouting incoherently at Elaine. Before Leann could intervene, Elaine burst into tears and ran out of the back yard. Vicky then turned and caught Leann's eye. She then began crying as well.

"Oh my gosh, Leann," Vicky wailed as she walked to the trio. She was sobbing uncontrollably. "I'm so sorry that I yelled at her at your wedding party. I just couldn't take it. Why was she even here?!"

Leann laughed, "Oh girl, I love you. It's fine." Leann hugged Vicky until she calmed down and Roger gave Vicky a high five.

The rest of the reception was nothing but joyful. Leann and James read scripted *love letters* to one another before they had their first dance. The letters had been missing only a few hours before, but the couple worked tirelessly to recreate them, so that all those in attendance would understand the love and commit-ment Leann and James had for one another.

A few weeks later, they headed to the white sandy beaches of Turks and Caicos to make their marriage official. Leann felt overwhelming gratitude for all that she had accomplished. All of her closest friends and family were there to celebrate yet another new chapter in her life. She was amazed that her part-time work as a consultant had financed both the reception and this dream destination wedding. Her mother never would have been able to join them if Leann's extra salary hadn't paid for her cruise ticket to the ceremony.

Leann's life had decidedly taken a turn for the positive in every regard. She tried not to question her good fortune and instead focused on all of the hard work she was investing in herself and her career. She felt that she could maintain her blessings as long as she was willing to continue learning and growing. Leann was focused on the positive so that's what she attracted.

Chapter 15

"She was unstoppable. Not because she did not have failures or doubts, but because she continued on despite them."

After their relaxing vacation in paradise, Leann and James returned to find her car in disrepair. Leann's brother Colin had taken her Trailblazer while they were away and abused it while joyriding with friends. Hannah was reluctant to explain how Colin had taken the car keys when she was housesitting, but there was no way of hiding the damage. Because of the blown transmission, Hannah couldn't get the car above 15mph on the ride home from the cruise port.

Things were made worse when a short time later, Leann found out that she had pre-cancer cells growing on her cervix. Thankfully she was able to receive an operation and get cleared by her doctors. They still worried that Leann may not fully recover and be able to conceive again.

Because of her troubles with her own fertility, Leann realized that she could give back to other women who had gone through even more harrowing situations. She decided to donate her eggs to women who were not able to have their own children. After a rigorous screening process, Leann was approved as a viable candidate as an egg donor.

After five years as a Pure Romance™ consultant, Leann decided to focus more attention on working with other women in the company and building a team. She quickly attracted dynamic women who wanted to make money, pay their way through college, find confidence and sisterhood, or get themselves out of debt.

Leann soon realized that she was empowering more and more women by offering them the opportunity to be consultants. After years of focusing on just making money at parties, Leann put an emphasis on supporting women who wanted be entrepreneurs. Her team went from a handful of women to a team 27 members strong in that first month.

The more Leann learned about the Pure Romance™ company, the more she understood that she could step into a leadership role and find financial freedom in a way that she had never imagined before. In her seventh year of business, Leann realized that she was making more money in a few hours a week as a consultant, than she was as a classroom teacher Monday through Friday.

That year she qualified for the Board of Directors in the company by making over $75,000 in personal sales, welcoming over 36 new team members, and meeting the team sales requirement of over $250,000. This position was considered prestigious, and came with extensive perks like travel and decision-making opportunities.

Shortly thereafter, Leann was shocked to find out she was pregnant again. She decided to keep it a secret until she could surprise James and Maddie. That surprise was derailed when she started having cramps and bleeding. Unfortunately, she soon found out that she had been pregnant with four embryos, but none of them seemed viable. Over the next few weeks, she learned that she had lost two of the babies. Eventually, doctors told her the two remaining babies had also died. Leann felt emotionally exhausted throughout the end of that school year.

She tried to stay positive through the miscarriages, a transition from full-time to part-time teaching, and move from a 5th grade position to a 7th grade position. Leann also continued growing her Pure Romance™ team, completing a demanding Master's Degree program, and tending to family responsibilities at home. Through it all, she returned to her inner light that continued to shine brightly. Leann knew that the challenges were exhausting, but were ultimately leading to more growth.

In the fall of 2014, Leann attended Oprah's "Live the Life You Want" weekend conference where she saw Elizabeth Gilbert speak about "following the whispers" that come up in your life. Leann didn't think much of the message at the time, but later listened to her intuition, and discovered that James was no longer taking his medication to treat his bipolar disorder. The resulting behaviors he demonstrated tested their marriage and led Leann to return to her a therapist from years earlier.

"Leann, I know this is a difficult time for you, but you need to focus on the things you can change or advance in *your* life instead of focusing on the aspects you have no control over," her therapist advised.

"What do you mean? This is my marriage!" Leann questioned. "How am I supposed to ignore the fact that James isn't taking his medicine like he promised he *always* would when we got married a year ago?"

"Leann, you cannot change James. You cannot want it more than he does. You both are going to make choices moving forward. You can focus on the things in life that you can control, like your business and being the best mother possible for Maddie."

Leann cried when she heard the options she was given, but she also knew that what her therapist was suggesting was true.

She had to move forward and pray that James would make the best choices for them as a family. Leann couldn't force her husband to change; he'd have to take those steps for himself.

Another whisper came to Leann when she realized that her life was changing in ways she didn't expect. As she focused even more time and attention on her blossoming team, she realized she might eventually have to step away from teaching completely if she was going to take her Pure Romance™ business to the next level.

In the spring of 2015, Leann graduated from McDaniels College on the Dean's List with her Master's degree in Curriculum Instruction. She crossed the stage that day with her grandma Eunice's photo tucked in her graduation cap while her father cheered loudly from the stands. Leann couldn't decide whether to cry at the thought of her absent grandparents, or laugh at her ridiculous father who made more noise than any other parent in attendance.

The next month she officially stepped away from her role as a classroom teacher at the end of the school year. Leann's life stabilized considerably as her father became a permanent fixture in her home, her mother celebrated five years drug-free, her daughter excelled in elementary school, and James again sought out treatment for his bipolar disorder.

Family and friends questioned her decision to walk away from teaching after all of her schooling and time in the classroom. Leann felt strongly that she would always remain a teacher, only now she'd educate women. In fact, she was asked to teach women throughout the country and Canada during subsequent years.

As confirmation of her leadership role in the company, Leann was asked to teach three workshops at the Pure Romance World Conference™ in Orlando, Florida in April 2016.

During that same international conference, Leann was recognized as a top global sponsor for the entire company, which included over 25,000 consultants. In 2015 alone, Leann sponsored 67 women and had team sales of $684, 121. Her personal sales topped $102,382.

At the end of the awards ceremony, Leann stood in front of 4,000 women holding all of her awards for her record-breaking accomplishments. In this moment everything became clear.

She knew the secret to her success.

Leann had believed in herself, even when others didn't; she had always known that she was meant to live a radiant life. Leann had always refused to be defined by her past or other people's expectations; instead, she let her light shine brightly.

It was never easy, but she never stopped.

When the whispers came, she listened.

She had needed a hero, so that's what she became.

Acknowledgments

Dad: We may have not been able to make lots of childhood memories but we sure do make a lot of great adulthood memories. Thank you for being my #1 cheerleader. I love making up for the missed time Daddyo!

Mom: I hope I make you proud, I know you are not proud of your past but I hope that you can make a future you are proud of. I am proud of the sobriety in your life today. Thank you for always loving me, even from afar growing up.

Grandma Margaret and Pop- Pop Jake: Some of my early years with you guys are the best memories I have of my childhood, I don't know if I ever told you, but thank you for rescuing me as child and letting me know what it felt like to be apart of a family. Being around you guys always made me feel loved. Pop- Pop always said to you, "we sure do have some great looking grandkids". I know he was always proud of each of us grandkids. Thank you grandma for continuing to cheer me on in life. You are always so proud of me with each accomplishment I make in life. It means the world to me and I know Pop Pop would be proud too.

Tom: You were always so wise and smart and could figure out any homework I had problems with. Thank you for being a positive role model in my life and always believing in me. I miss you.

Grandmom Eunice: So many days I find myself thinking about you and what you would say if you were here now. I will always cherish the time we had together and the love you had for me. You always knew I would do anything I put my mind to. I hope you are up there smiling down proud as can be.

Siblings: We may only be connected by our dads but it still makes us connected. Remember to not let your past define your future. You guys are all better than that. Make yourself proud, that's all you need.

Victoria: Life will always be a roller coaster but you have to be ready for those bumps. Always remember you have a daughter to make proud now. I'll always be here cheering you on! I believe in you to make all your dreams a reality.

Ms. Wicks: I really wish I could find you and just let you know how much you meant to me growing up. You are the only teacher that made such a lasting impression on me. I became a teacher because I wanted to change lives the way you changed mine. If I ever got the chance to find you and see you, I would give you the biggest hug and bring you homemade cookies like we made all those years ago.

Melinda & Family: I love being your adopted daughter. Thank you for always treating me like your own. I loved having you as my adopted Mom #2 growing up. You and your family always treated me as though I was part of the family. Thanks for being there when I needed it the most.

Cheryl: From a young age, you were the light I needed to get me through some of my hardest years growing up. You always knew I was destined for greatness. You always reminded me how to stand tall and continue on my journey despite what others said around me. Thank you for always believing in me!

Stacey: You always are there to laugh at my stories and shake your head in disbelief at my stories. You always said each time we catch up, "you need to write a book". Well girl, I did! Thanks for always being my wings when I have felt like they were broke over the years. I love having you as my best friend. I love watching our girls grow up and have an unstoppable friendship like we have.

Nicki: The memories don't stop with you. The tears, the laughs and craziness we had together growing up. Time goes by quick and I love that when we catch up, it's like not even a day has gone by. Thanks for being a great friend through the highs and lows. oxox

Tricia: I love the memories we have in our younger years and the friendship we have developed over the years. I look forward to our lunch dates where we sit and chat for hours. Thank you for always cheering me on in everything I do and telling me when you think I'm being ridiculous.

John: You have been seen me grow so much in the last 14 years we have known each other. Thank you for always supporting me in everything I have done in life and continue to do. Thanks for being by my side through it all and being a great dad to Madison. I love all of your family like my own and your family has always loved me as their own. I will always love you.

Madison: As a child you might think you need me, but you have it all wrong. I need you! You have made me strive for excellence in my own life. You have given me strength to always push forward and treat each day as a blessing. I hope I always continue to make you proud. I love being your mom!

Teacher Friends: Whenever I need a good laugh, I think of some of the funniest stories we share as teachers. The kind that nobody would believe unless they worked at our school. You each have made a difference in my life by inspiring children to chase their dreams and that they are valued.

Previous students: I hope beyond the lessons that I had taught that you may have forgotten, you always remember one lesson: Through hard work and determination you can do anything and be anything you put your mind to in life. Surround yourself with people who have similar goals and dreams and support yours.

#Besties: I am grateful to have met each of you in this business. I love the bond we have! We have each other's back at all times even if it takes an hour to catch up on the group text each day. You ladies are cherished and never replaceable.

PR Decadent Dynasty Team: You ladies tell me all the time I inspire you, but you have it all wrong...YOU each inspire me and motivate me. I love being your cheerleader and watching and helping you grow. Without you, I would have no purpose as a leader; you continue to make me proud every day. I'm honored to be your leader.

PR sisters: When you join Pure Romance, you don't just get a business, you get the most amazing and supportive sisterhood that a girl could ever imagine. I am blessed to have each of you in my life. My heart is so full knowing I am surrounded by a tribe of amazing ladies that inspire and empower each other daily.

Pure Romance Corporate Office: Patty & Chris and the VIP team and all those who work at corporate: Thank you. Thank you for taking us under your wing and treating us like family when you adopted us. Each and every day I am reminded of truly how amazing it is to work for a company that cares about us and treats us like royalty. I didn't realize how much I was missing until Pure Romance blessed my life and my family. I am able to live a life by design and a life beyond my wildest dreams growing up and I just want you to know I will forever be grateful.

To my friends, family, hostesses, clients, followers and supporters: you will never know how much you believing in me and your support means. I hope I continue to bring a smile to your face when you hear my name. I love each of you!

Elaine: I forgive you.

"James" & Leann's (Actual) Love Letters...

James:

To my beautiful, amazing, stunning future bride:

Today we get to stand together before our family members, closest friends and loved ones to celebrate our love for each other. When we first agreed to write these to each other, I'll admit I was a little nervous but also excited to express how I feel about you. To sit here and say that I have been looking forward to the day we say I do would be a MASSIVE UNDERSTATEMENT. I am overwhelmed at how unbelievably blessed I am to have you in my life now and forever. I not only get to marry the love of my life but also my best friend. I know that this is just the beginning and I look forward to our future together with the same passion, love and hope that I have looked at so far. I know there will be struggles, difficulties and stress in our future but I look forward to those times as not as a bad time but as a time to build our relationship stronger then it is now. Your kind heart, energetic personality, and total unconditional love for me shows me every day that my decision to spend the rest of my life with you is the correct one.

I want you to know that I am not perfect and will not always have the best answer, or know how to handle certain situations. I am a proud person, quick tempered and stubborn. I am assured that your presence in my life will make me a stronger and better man. I promise to be a loving husband, confident leader and a great a caring dad to our beautiful daughter Madison. Through any difficult times please remember that I love you passionately and will do everything and anything in my power to be the best man I can to you and our daughter moving forward in our live together.

I wake up every day amazed that a beautiful, intelligent and loving woman like you wants to spend the rest of her life with me. And saying beautiful is just an understatement! After all those moments of amazement pass, I am reminded that you are not just any women you, LEANN, are more than I could have ever dreamed of! To stand here and say that I am blessed could not fully express all my feelings for you, neither can this letter. I trust you with my life completely and fully and the journey ahead of us is for both of us not just one or the other. We started young and now have the chance to grow old together. I was searching on the internet for a really good quote to put in this letter but all I kept reading were the words "I love you because I need you". That same sentence appeared in everything I read. So I sat down and read it over and over again, just that sentence. I began to think hmmmmmmmmm that phrase sounds kind of selfish to love someone because you need them? This didn't explain how I felt at all so I flipped it to say "I need you, because I love you" so I am standing here today telling you I need you more than I have ever needed another person. From the day of our wedding we are one and I couldn't be more excited to hear that phrase and answer with the most beautiful 2 words I can say to you that day "I do".

Love your future husband,

"James"

Leann:

Dear "James",

Can you believe this love story of ours started by seeing you drive by on Ritchie Hwy? For once in my life I'm right where I want to be. I have always desired to have that special someone in my life who could make me feel like everything was alright in this world, when I'm with you, this is something that I feel each day. The greatest relationships are the ones you never expected to be in, the ones that swept you off your feet.

You give me bravery I have never known. You give me courage and strength to fight the only fear I could not face on my own- the fear of love. I've watched every relationship I have ever known crumble to the ground when the foundation was shaken. No one attempts to fix what's broken anymore, they just abandon it. I've watched it happen time after time, even in my own life. It's the reason why I never believed in things like love, marriage, or forever. But you changed that. You gave me hope. When I look at you I see my future. When I look at you I get a glimpse of forever. Never give up on love, because when things get rough in life it's just testing us out making us stronger. Like all true romances, we have had a lot to overcome, and we did with much love and acceptance. They say what matters is if the one who you love stands by you in times of need rather than in times of joy. You have always been by my side and never let me go. I love you for all that you have done for me, no one and nothing else can ever take your place. Even when I wanted to give up because that was easier, you fought with all you had for me. I thank you for that because we might not be here today if you didn't. Love is a feeling, marriage is a contract and relationships are work. Almost 10 years together and we have shared it all. The ups the downs the joys, the tears, in the end we are stronger.

In truth, I am marrying my prince charming- but a prince who is also human, who has faults and issues just like every person, no matter how wonderful he is. Same goes for me, knowing each other's imperfections and that life will not be always perfect but as long as we are together it will be perfect for us. We come to love not by finding a perfect person, but by learning to see an imperfect person perfectly, this is how I know that our love was written in the stars up and above and that there could never be another love for either of us and we were destined to be.

There are days when I lie in bed, consumed by thoughts of you, the way your blue eyes light up when you smile, the sweet messages you send me throughout the day, how when tickle me when I'm laughing too hard to say stop, or Madison crawls in our bed and we are all watching Full House together and this makes me feel like I'm right where I belong. I may not be able to tell you enough just how much you mean to me, so today I want to tell you in this letter that having you walk into my life is probably the best thing that could have ever happened to me.

Thinking about all the journeys we have made together, all the dreams that we have shared and the life that we have made for ourselves, makes me feel thankful and blessed, I am lucky to have you as my partner for life, there is no one else who could have ever loved me the way you do. We are strong, and we can make it through together and that life is going to be quite a ride with you, the kind that I'm looking forward to. So today I make a promise to you that come hell or high waters you will always find me by your side. I truly love you and look forward to spending the rest of my life with you and the family and life we have created.

Our song fits us perfect, God did bless the broken road the always led me back to you.

Love Always,

Leann

WE DON'T MEET PEOPLE BY COINCIDENCE, THEY ARE MEANT TO CROSS OUR PATH FOR A REASON.

BLINKSOFLIFE

Meet the Team behind Leann's Rise Up, Shine On

Pamela Cross: Owner/Stylist of Blown 25 Hair Studios
8207 Fort Smallwood Rd, Baltimore MD 21226
443-305-2686
Hair & Makeup of Leann Rhodes on the book cover done by Pamela Cross

Megan Hicks: MLH Photography
Email:mlhcaptureit@gmail.com
www.meganhicksphotography.com
Cover photo of Leann Rhodes taken by Megan
Hicks

Amy Brooks: Author, Public Speaker&Writing Coach

Ghost Writer for Leann Rhodes' Rise Up, Shine

www.amyrbrooks.com

amyreneebrooks@gmail.com

DK Walker: Owner & Operator of En El Publishing Services & En El Publishing Author/Blogger and all around great guy

Designed Leann's book cover for print and eBook versions, also formatted interior files for eBook and typeset for print version.
www.enelpublishingservices.com
Email:enelpublishingservices@enelpublishing.com
Phone Number 202-705-5243

Wanna get connected with Leann?
Well make sure you follow or friend
her on social media...

Facebook: Leann Rhodes Ickes
Twitter: @LeanRhodes13
Instagram: pureromance_Leann
Blog: www.designingthelifeyoulove.com
Snapchat: LeannRhodes1

So many people, memories, and moments have played a huge part in Leann's life, always helping her to Rise Up, Shine On. Now she wants to share some of these great memories and people with you...

About The Author

Leann has been successful as a student, a classroom teacher, and now as an entrepreneur. She has finally found her passion in empowering women through Pure Romance™ and sharing her personal story. She plans to reach an even wider audience with this book and future speaking engagements.

Leann has resided in Anne Arundel County, Maryland her entire life. She currently lives in a happy house full of family, two bulldogs named Pearl and Roxi, and two cats named Cookie and Chance.

Leann needs your help!

The most important thing to an author are book reviews; and if Rise Up, Shine On was inspirational to you as it has been to so many others, Leann would really appreciate you leaving her a review on Amazon or Goodreads.

Leann loves hearing back personally from her readers as well and can be reached at riseupshineon@gmail.com and promises to answer each email.

Leann also would like to take this time and acknowledge John Mayer, Anne Lamott, Beau Taplin and the rest of the wonderful people (who unfortunately are unknown) for the quotes which appear in Rise Up, Shine On.

Your quotes resonated deeply with me and their usage here in my book is deeply appreciated.

Made in the USA
Middletown, DE
23 May 2018